Life to the Fullest:

A daily journal for purposeful joy & growth

Name:

_____

Email Address:

_____

Date I Started My Journal:

_____

Date I Finished My Journal:

_____

"I have come that they
may have life, and
have it to the full."
—Jesus (Jn. 10:10)

Why I Created This Journal...

As a person who has always loved writing, I wanted to practice placing a purposeful focus on my physical, mental, and spiritual health via a reasonably priced, practical journal. However, I couldn't seem to find what I wanted online or in stores! Because of this, I decided to create my own daily journal—and I loved using it. That was when it occurred to me that I could make the journal available to others so that they could use it, too.

I wanted to make sure it was more than just a journal. I wanted it to include helpful writing prompts, a way to track prayer requests, personal notes, daily exercise, and more. I wanted a clean, cool journal that I would personally like to carry around throughout the day. This journal is made to be just that—for toting around while jotting down notes and inspirations, for filling in the daily blanks as the day goes along, for quiet time with morning coffee, or for peaceful reflections at night. You can also fill in the sections by yourself, with a spouse, or with your family to create a devotional time.

Research shows that making an effort to identify what you are thankful for on a regular basis leads to increased happiness. I believe this is because we were made to give thanks (Colossians 4:2)! Everything in this book is designed to promote a better YOU—mind, body, and spirit—so try to fill out as much as you can. However, don't get overwhelmed. If you can't fill in every section every day, that is perfectly all right. This is YOUR book.

If this book helps someone else with personal growth the way it has helped me, it was well worth the effort. My hope is that this will be a helpful tool to guide you in finding renewed focus on meeting your daily goals and reflecting on who you want to be. Happy journaling!

—Rachel

Connect with me on Instagram @rach_roams!

Rachel L. Giles is currently earning her Doctorate in Higher Education Leadership and has previously earned a Master of Arts degree in Communication Studies, a Bachelor of Arts degree in Communication Studies, and an Associate of Arts degree in English/Creative Writing. Rachel has extensively studied leadership and has instructed students in university courses including: digital writing and production, decision-making in small groups, and public speaking. She is currently living her best life with her husband and the love of her life, Jeremiah, in a small island beach town in the Southern U.S. She loves writing, traveling the world, finding her purpose in helping others, coffee dates with friends, healthy living, and creativity.

My Bucket List For This Year

Your list of things to do before this year kicks the bucket! (This may include self-improvement, facing fears, books to read, professional goals, etc.)

Inspirational Quotes & Scripture

In this space, write down words that inspire you, from your favorite verses to insprational quotes from speakers. When you need encouragement, flip back to this page and find it here!

My Life: BIG Goals & Dreams

In this section, you can write down some of the BIGGEST long-term goals and dreams you have for your life. "May He give you the desire of your heart and make all your plans succeed." –Ps. 20:4

BIG Dreams:

Steps I'm Taking to Achieve My Big Dreams:

How I Can Help Others By Achieving My Big Dreams:

Notes

Today's Entry

Date:_____ Exercise:_____ Water Intake: (1)(2)(3)(4)(5)(6)(7)(8)

5 Things I'm Thankful For:

1._____
2._____
3._____
4._____
5._____

My Quote Of The Day:

Today's Bible Reading (References & Notes):

_____
_____
_____

Prayer Requests/BIG Dreams:

_____
_____
_____

How I'm Feeling Today (Circle All That Apply):

* Happy * Stressed/Anxious * Peaceful * Tired
*Thankful * Sad * Angry *Lonely * Relieved
* Other:

Answers To Prayer:

_____
_____

What's Bothering Me:

_____
_____

How I Can Resolve It (Or Pray About It):

_____
_____

Thoughts & Prayer:

_____
_____
_____
_____
_____
_____
_____
_____

Today's Entry

Date:_____ Exercise:_____ Water Intake: (1)(2)(3)(4)(5)(6)(7)(8)

5 Things I'm Thankful For:

1._____
2._____
3._____
4._____
5._____

My Quote Of The Day:

Today's Bible Reading (References & Notes):

_____
_____
_____

Prayer Requests/BIG Dreams:

_____
_____
_____

How I'm Feeling Today (Circle All That Apply):

* Happy * Stressed/Anxious * Peaceful * Tired
*Thankful * Sad * Angry *Lonely * Relieved
* Other:

Answers To Prayer:

_____
_____
_____

What's Bothering Me:

_____
_____

How I Can Resolve It (Or Pray About It):

_____
_____

Thoughts & Prayer:

_____
_____
_____
_____
_____
_____
_____
_____

Today's Entry

Date:_____   Exercise:_____   Water Intake: (1)(2)(3)(4)(5)(6)(7)(8)

5 Things I'm Thankful For:

1._____
2._____
3._____
4._____
5._____

My Quote Of The Day:

Today's Bible Reading (References & Notes):

_____
_____
_____

Prayer Requests/BIG Dreams:

_____
_____
_____

How I'm Feeling Today (Circle All That Apply):

* Happy * Stressed/Anxious * Peaceful * Tired
*Thankful * Sad * Angry *Lonely * Relieved
* Other:

Answers To Prayer:

_____
_____
_____

What's Bothering Me:

_____
_____

How I Can Resolve It (Or Pray About It):

_____
_____

Thoughts & Prayer:

_____
_____
_____
_____
_____
_____
_____
_____

Today's Entry

Date:_____   Exercise:_____   Water Intake: (1)(2)(3)(4)(5)(6)(7)(8)

5 Things I'm Thankful For:

1._____
2._____
3._____
4._____
5._____

My Quote Of The Day:

Today's Bible Reading (References & Notes):

_____
_____
_____

Prayer Requests/BIG Dreams:

_____
_____
_____

How I'm Feeling Today (Circle All That Apply):

* Happy * Stressed/Anxious * Peaceful * Tired
*Thankful * Sad * Angry *Lonely * Relieved
* Other:

Answers To Prayer:

_____
_____
_____

What's Bothering Me:

_____
_____

How I Can Resolve It (Or Pray About It):

_____
_____

Thoughts & Prayer:

_____
_____
_____
_____
_____
_____
_____
_____

Today's Entry

Date:_____ Exercise:_____ Water Intake: (1)(2)(3)(4)(5)(6)(7)(8)

5 Things I'm Thankful For:

1._____
2._____
3._____
4._____
5._____

My Quote Of The Day:

Today's Bible Reading (References & Notes):

_____
_____
_____

Prayer Requests/BIG Dreams:

_____
_____
_____

How I'm Feeling Today (Circle All That Apply):

* Happy * Stressed/Anxious * Peaceful * Tired
*Thankful * Sad * Angry *Lonely * Relieved
* Other:

Answers To Prayer:

_____
_____
_____

What's Bothering Me:

_____
_____

How I Can Resolve It (Or Pray About It):

_____
_____

Thoughts & Prayer:

_____
_____
_____
_____
_____
_____
_____
_____

Today's Entry

Date:_____ Exercise:_____ Water Intake: (1)(2)(3)(4)(5)(6)(7)(8)

5 Things I'm Thankful For:

1._____
2._____
3._____
4._____
5._____

My Quote Of The Day:

Today's Bible Reading (References & Notes):

_____
_____
_____

Prayer Requests/BIG Dreams:

_____
_____
_____

How I'm Feeling Today (Circle All That Apply):

* Happy * Stressed/Anxious * Peaceful * Tired
*Thankful * Sad * Angry *Lonely * Relieved
* Other:

Answers To Prayer:

_____
_____
_____

What's Bothering Me:

_____
_____

How I Can Resolve It (Or Pray About It):

_____
_____

Thoughts & Prayer:

_____
_____
_____
_____
_____
_____
_____
_____

Today's Entry

Date:_____   Exercise:_____   Water Intake: (1)(2)(3)(4)(5)(6)(7)(8)

5 Things I'm Thankful For:

1._____
2._____
3._____
4._____
5._____

My Quote Of The Day:

Today's Bible Reading (References & Notes):

_____
_____
_____

Prayer Requests/BIG Dreams:

_____
_____
_____

How I'm Feeling Today (Circle All That Apply):

* Happy * Stressed/Anxious * Peaceful * Tired
*Thankful * Sad * Angry *Lonely * Relieved
* Other:

Answers To Prayer:

_____
_____
_____

What's Bothering Me:

_____
_____

How I Can Resolve It (Or Pray About It):

_____
_____

Thoughts & Prayer:

_____
_____
_____
_____
_____
_____
_____
_____

Today's Entry

Date:_____   Exercise:_____   Water Intake: (1)(2)(3)(4)(5)(6)(7)(8)

5 Things I'm Thankful For:

1._____
2._____
3._____
4._____
5._____

My Quote Of The Day:

Today's Bible Reading (References & Notes):

_____
_____
_____

Prayer Requests/BIG Dreams:

_____
_____
_____

How I'm Feeling Today (Circle All That Apply):

* Happy * Stressed/Anxious * Peaceful * Tired
*Thankful * Sad * Angry *Lonely * Relieved
* Other:

Answers To Prayer:

_____
_____
_____

What's Bothering Me:

_____
_____

How I Can Resolve It (Or Pray About It):

_____
_____

Thoughts & Prayer:

_____
_____
_____
_____
_____
_____
_____
_____

Today's Entry

Date:_____   Exercise:_____   Water Intake: (1)(2)(3)(4)(5)(6)(7)(8)

5 Things I'm Thankful For:

1._____
2._____
3._____
4._____
5._____

My Quote Of The Day:

Today's Bible Reading (References & Notes):

_____
_____
_____

Prayer Requests/BIG Dreams:

_____
_____
_____

How I'm Feeling Today (Circle All That Apply):

* Happy * Stressed/Anxious * Peaceful * Tired
*Thankful * Sad * Angry *Lonely * Relieved
* Other:

Answers To Prayer:

_____
_____
_____

What's Bothering Me:

_____
_____

How I Can Resolve It (Or Pray About It):

_____
_____

Thoughts & Prayer:

_____
_____
_____
_____
_____
_____
_____
_____

Today's Entry

Date:_____   Exercise:_____   Water Intake: (1)(2)(3)(4)(5)(6)(7)(8)

5 Things I'm Thankful For:

1._____
2._____
3._____
4._____
5._____

My Quote Of The Day:

Today's Bible Reading (References & Notes):

_____
_____
_____
_____

Prayer Requests/BIG Dreams:

_____
_____
_____
_____

How I'm Feeling Today (Circle All That Apply):

* Happy * Stressed/Anxious * Peaceful * Tired
*Thankful * Sad * Angry *Lonely * Relieved
* Other:

Answers To Prayer:

_____
_____

What's Bothering Me:

_____
_____

How I Can Resolve It (Or Pray About It):

_____
_____

Thoughts & Prayer:

_____
_____
_____
_____
_____
_____
_____
_____

Today's Entry

Date:_____   Exercise:_____   Water Intake: (1)(2)(3)(4)(5)(6)(7)(8)

5 Things I'm Thankful For:

1._____
2._____
3._____
4._____
5._____

My Quote Of The Day:

Today's Bible Reading (References & Notes):

_____
_____
_____
_____

Prayer Requests/BIG Dreams:

_____
_____
_____

How I'm Feeling Today (Circle All That Apply):

* Happy * Stressed/Anxious * Peaceful * Tired
*Thankful * Sad * Angry *Lonely * Relieved
* Other:

Answers To Prayer:

_____
_____
_____

What's Bothering Me:

_____
_____

How I Can Resolve It (Or Pray About It):

_____
_____

Thoughts & Prayer:

_____
_____
_____
_____
_____
_____
_____
_____

Today's Entry

Date:_____ Exercise:_____ Water Intake: (1)(2)(3)(4)(5)(6)(7)(8)

5 Things I'm Thankful For:

1._____
2._____
3._____
4._____
5._____

My Quote Of The Day:

Today's Bible Reading (References & Notes):

_____
_____
_____

Prayer Requests/BIG Dreams:

_____
_____
_____

How I'm Feeling Today (Circle All That Apply):

* Happy * Stressed/Anxious * Peaceful * Tired
*Thankful * Sad * Angry *Lonely * Relieved
* Other:

Answers To Prayer:

_____
_____
_____

What's Bothering Me:

_____
_____

How I Can Resolve It (Or Pray About It):

_____
_____

Thoughts & Prayer:

_____
_____
_____
_____
_____
_____
_____
_____

Today's Entry

Date:_____ Exercise:_____ Water Intake: (1)(2)(3)(4)(5)(6)(7)(8)

5 Things I'm Thankful For:

1._____
2._____
3._____
4._____
5._____

My Quote Of The Day:

Today's Bible Reading (References & Notes):

_____
_____
_____

Prayer Requests/BIG Dreams:

_____
_____
_____

How I'm Feeling Today (Circle All That Apply):

* Happy * Stressed/Anxious * Peaceful * Tired
*Thankful * Sad * Angry *Lonely * Relieved
* Other:

Answers To Prayer:

_____
_____
_____

What's Bothering Me:

_____
_____

How I Can Resolve It (Or Pray About It):

_____
_____

Thoughts & Prayer:

_____
_____
_____
_____
_____
_____
_____
_____

Today's Entry

Date:_____   Exercise:_____   Water Intake: (1)(2)(3)(4)(5)(6)(7)(8)

5 Things I'm Thankful For:

1._____
2._____
3._____
4._____
5._____

My Quote Of The Day:

Today's Bible Reading (References & Notes):

_____
_____
_____

Prayer Requests/BIG Dreams:

_____
_____
_____

How I'm Feeling Today (Circle All That Apply):

* Happy * Stressed/Anxious * Peaceful * Tired
*Thankful * Sad * Angry *Lonely * Relieved
* Other:

Answers To Prayer:

_____
_____
_____

What's Bothering Me:

_____
_____

How I Can Resolve It (Or Pray About It):

_____
_____

Thoughts & Prayer:

_____
_____
_____
_____
_____
_____
_____
_____

Today's Entry

Date:_____ Exercise:_____ Water Intake: (1)(2)(3)(4)(5)(6)(7)(8)

5 Things I'm Thankful For:

1._____
2._____
3._____
4._____
5._____

My Quote Of The Day:

Today's Bible Reading (References & Notes):

_____
_____
_____

Prayer Requests/BIG Dreams:

_____
_____
_____

How I'm Feeling Today (Circle All That Apply):

* Happy * Stressed/Anxious * Peaceful * Tired
*Thankful * Sad * Angry *Lonely * Relieved
* Other:

Answers To Prayer:

_____
_____
_____

What's Bothering Me:

_____
_____

How I Can Resolve It (Or Pray About It):

_____
_____

Thoughts & Prayer:

_____
_____
_____
_____
_____
_____
_____
_____

Today's Entry

Date:_____   Exercise:_____   Water Intake: (1)(2)(3)(4)(5)(6)(7)(8)

5 Things I'm Thankful For:

1._____
2._____
3._____
4._____
5._____

My Quote Of The Day:

Today's Bible Reading (References & Notes):

_____
_____
_____

Prayer Requests/BIG Dreams:

_____
_____
_____

How I'm Feeling Today (Circle All That Apply):

* Happy * Stressed/Anxious * Peaceful * Tired
*Thankful * Sad * Angry *Lonely * Relieved
* Other:

Answers To Prayer:

_____
_____
_____

What's Bothering Me:

_____
_____

How I Can Resolve It (Or Pray About It):

_____
_____
_____

Thoughts & Prayer:

_____
_____
_____
_____
_____
_____
_____
_____

Today's Entry

Date:_____   Exercise:_____   Water Intake: (1)(2)(3)(4)(5)(6)(7)(8)

5 Things I'm Thankful For:

1._____

2._____

3._____

4._____

5._____

My Quote Of The Day:

Today's Bible Reading (References & Notes):

_____

_____

_____

Prayer Requests/BIG Dreams:

_____

_____

_____

How I'm Feeling Today (Circle All That Apply):

* Happy * Stressed/Anxious * Peaceful * Tired

*Thankful * Sad * Angry *Lonely * Relieved

* Other:

Answers To Prayer:

_____

_____

_____

What's Bothering Me:

_____

_____

How I Can Resolve It (Or Pray About It):

_____

_____

Thoughts & Prayer:

_____

_____

_____

_____

_____

_____

_____

_____

Today's Entry

Date:_____   Exercise:_____   Water Intake: (1)(2)(3)(4)(5)(6)(7)(8)

5 Things I'm Thankful For:

1._____
2._____
3._____
4._____
5._____

My Quote Of The Day:

Today's Bible Reading (References & Notes):

_____
_____
_____
_____

Prayer Requests/BIG Dreams:

_____
_____
_____
_____

How I'm Feeling Today (Circle All That Apply):

* Happy * Stressed/Anxious * Peaceful * Tired
*Thankful * Sad * Angry *Lonely * Relieved
* Other:

Answers To Prayer:

_____
_____
_____

What's Bothering Me:

_____
_____

How I Can Resolve It (Or Pray About It):

_____
_____

Thoughts & Prayer:

_____
_____
_____
_____
_____
_____
_____
_____

Today's Entry

Date:_____ Exercise:_____ Water Intake: (1)(2)(3)(4)(5)(6)(7)(8)

5 Things I'm Thankful For:

1._____
2._____
3._____
4._____
5._____

My Quote Of The Day:

Today's Bible Reading (References & Notes):

_____
_____
_____

Prayer Requests/BIG Dreams:

_____
_____
_____

How I'm Feeling Today (Circle All That Apply):

* Happy * Stressed/Anxious * Peaceful * Tired
*Thankful * Sad * Angry *Lonely * Relieved
* Other:

Answers To Prayer:

_____
_____
_____

What's Bothering Me:

_____
_____

How I Can Resolve It (Or Pray About It):

_____
_____

Thoughts & Prayer:

_____
_____
_____
_____
_____
_____
_____
_____

Today's Entry

*Date:*_____ *Exercise:*_____ *Water Intake: (1)(2)(3)(4)(5)(6)(7)(8)*

5 Things I'm Thankful For:

1._____
2._____
3._____
4._____
5._____

My Quote Of The Day:

Today's Bible Reading (References & Notes):

_____
_____
_____

Prayer Requests/BIG Dreams:

_____
_____
_____

How I'm Feeling Today (Circle All That Apply):

* Happy * Stressed/Anxious * Peaceful * Tired
*Thankful * Sad * Angry *Lonely * Relieved
* Other:

Answers To Prayer:

_____
_____
_____

What's Bothering Me:

_____
_____

How I Can Resolve It (Or Pray About It):

_____
_____

Thoughts & Prayer:

_____
_____
_____
_____
_____
_____
_____
_____

Today's Entry

Date:_____   Exercise:_____   Water Intake: (1)(2)(3)(4)(5)(6)(7)(8)

5 Things I'm Thankful For:

1._____
2._____
3._____
4._____
5._____

My Quote Of The Day:

Today's Bible Reading (References & Notes):

_____
_____
_____

Prayer Requests/BIG Dreams:

_____
_____
_____

How I'm Feeling Today (Circle All That Apply):

* Happy * Stressed/Anxious * Peaceful * Tired
*Thankful * Sad * Angry *Lonely * Relieved
* Other:

Answers To Prayer:

_____
_____
_____

What's Bothering Me:

_____
_____

How I Can Resolve It (Or Pray About It):

_____
_____

Thoughts & Prayer:

_____
_____
_____
_____
_____
_____
_____

Today's Entry

Date:_____ Exercise:_____ Water Intake: (1)(2)(3)(4)(5)(6)(7)(8)

5 Things I'm Thankful For:

1._____
2._____
3._____
4._____
5._____

My Quote Of The Day:

Today's Bible Reading (References & Notes):

_____
_____
_____

Prayer Requests/BIG Dreams:

_____
_____
_____

How I'm Feeling Today (Circle All That Apply):

* Happy * Stressed/Anxious * Peaceful * Tired
*Thankful * Sad * Angry *Lonely * Relieved
* Other:

Answers To Prayer:

_____
_____
_____

What's Bothering Me:

_____
_____

How I Can Resolve It (Or Pray About It):

_____
_____

Thoughts & Prayer:

_____
_____
_____
_____
_____
_____
_____
_____

Today's Entry

Date:_____ Exercise:_____ Water Intake: (1)(2)(3)(4)(5)(6)(7)(8)

5 Things I'm Thankful For:

1._____
2._____
3._____
4._____
5._____

My Quote Of The Day:

Today's Bible Reading (References & Notes):

_____
_____
_____

Prayer Requests/BIG Dreams:

_____
_____
_____

How I'm Feeling Today (Circle All That Apply):

* Happy * Stressed/Anxious * Peaceful * Tired
*Thankful * Sad * Angry *Lonely * Relieved
* Other:

Answers To Prayer:

_____
_____
_____

What's Bothering Me:

_____
_____

How I Can Resolve It (Or Pray About It):

_____
_____

Thoughts & Prayer:

_____
_____
_____
_____
_____
_____
_____
_____

Today's Entry

Date:_____ Exercise:_____ Water Intake: (1)(2)(3)(4)(5)(6)(7)(8)

5 Things I'm Thankful For:

1._____
2._____
3._____
4._____
5._____

My Quote Of The Day:

Today's Bible Reading (References & Notes):

_____
_____
_____
_____

Prayer Requests/BIG Dreams:

_____
_____
_____
_____

How I'm Feeling Today (Circle All That Apply):

* Happy * Stressed/Anxious * Peaceful * Tired
*Thankful * Sad * Angry *Lonely * Relieved
* Other:

Answers To Prayer:

_____
_____

What's Bothering Me:

_____
_____

How I Can Resolve It (Or Pray About It):

_____
_____

Thoughts & Prayer:

_____
_____
_____
_____
_____
_____
_____
_____

Today's Entry

Date:_____ Exercise:_____ Water Intake: (1)(2)(3)(4)(5)(6)(7)(8)

5 Things I'm Thankful For:

1._____
2._____
3._____
4._____
5._____

My Quote Of The Day:

Today's Bible Reading (References & Notes):

_____
_____
_____

Prayer Requests/BIG Dreams:

_____
_____
_____

How I'm Feeling Today (Circle All That Apply):

* Happy * Stressed/Anxious * Peaceful * Tired
*Thankful * Sad * Angry *Lonely * Relieved
* Other:

Answers To Prayer:

_____
_____
_____

What's Bothering Me:

_____
_____

How I Can Resolve It (Or Pray About It):

_____
_____

Thoughts & Prayer:

_____
_____
_____
_____
_____
_____
_____
_____

Today's Entry

Date:_____   Exercise:_____   Water Intake: (1)(2)(3)(4)(5)(6)(7)(8)

5 Things I'm Thankful For:

1._____
2._____
3._____
4._____
5._____

My Quote Of The Day:

Today's Bible Reading (References & Notes):

_____
_____
_____

Prayer Requests/BIG Dreams:

_____
_____
_____

How I'm Feeling Today (Circle All That Apply):

* Happy * Stressed/Anxious * Peaceful * Tired
*Thankful * Sad * Angry *Lonely * Relieved
* Other:

Answers To Prayer:

_____
_____
_____

What's Bothering Me:

_____
_____

How I Can Resolve It (Or Pray About It):

_____
_____

Thoughts & Prayer:

_____
_____
_____
_____
_____
_____
_____
_____

Today's Entry

Date:_____ Exercise:_____ Water Intake: (1)(2)(3)(4)(5)(6)(7)(8)

5 Things I'm Thankful For:

1._____
2._____
3._____
4._____
5._____

My Quote Of The Day:

Today's Bible Reading (References & Notes):

_____
_____
_____

Prayer Requests/BIG Dreams:

_____
_____
_____

How I'm Feeling Today (Circle All That Apply):

* Happy * Stressed/Anxious * Peaceful * Tired
*Thankful * Sad * Angry *Lonely * Relieved
* Other:

Answers To Prayer:

_____
_____
_____

What's Bothering Me:

_____
_____

How I Can Resolve It (Or Pray About It):

_____
_____

Thoughts & Prayer:

_____
_____
_____
_____
_____
_____
_____
_____

"...His peace will
guard your hearts and
minds as you live in
Christ Jesus."
(Phil. 4:7)

Today's Entry

Date:_____ Exercise:_____ Water Intake: (1)(2)(3)(4)(5)(6)(7)(8)

5 Things I'm Thankful For:

1._____
2._____
3._____
4._____
5._____

My Quote Of The Day:

Today's Bible Reading (References & Notes):

_____
_____
_____

Prayer Requests/BIG Dreams:

_____
_____
_____

How I'm Feeling Today (Circle All That Apply):

* Happy * Stressed/Anxious * Peaceful * Tired
*Thankful * Sad * Angry *Lonely * Relieved
* Other:

Answers To Prayer:

_____
_____
_____

What's Bothering Me:

_____
_____

How I Can Resolve It (Or Pray About It):

_____
_____

Thoughts & Prayer:

_____
_____
_____
_____
_____
_____
_____
_____

Today's Entry

Date:_____   Exercise:_____   Water Intake: (1)(2)(3)(4)(5)(6)(7)(8)

5 Things I'm Thankful For:

1._____
2._____
3._____
4._____
5._____

My Quote Of The Day:

Today's Bible Reading (References & Notes):

_____
_____
_____
_____

Prayer Requests/BIG Dreams:

_____
_____
_____
_____

How I'm Feeling Today (Circle All That Apply):

* Happy * Stressed/Anxious * Peaceful * Tired
*Thankful * Sad * Angry *Lonely * Relieved
* Other:

Answers To Prayer:

_____
_____
_____

What's Bothering Me:

_____
_____

How I Can Resolve It (Or Pray About It):

_____
_____
_____

Thoughts & Prayer:

_____
_____
_____
_____
_____
_____
_____
_____
_____

Today's Entry

Date:_____   Exercise:_____   Water Intake: (1)(2)(3)(4)(5)(6)(7)(8)

5 Things I'm Thankful For:

1._____
2._____
3._____
4._____
5._____

My Quote Of The Day:

Today's Bible Reading (References & Notes):

_____
_____
_____

Prayer Requests/BIG Dreams:

_____
_____
_____

How I'm Feeling Today (Circle All That Apply):

* Happy * Stressed/Anxious * Peaceful * Tired
*Thankful * Sad * Angry *Lonely * Relieved
* Other:

Answers To Prayer:

_____
_____
_____

What's Bothering Me:

_____
_____

How I Can Resolve It (Or Pray About It):

_____
_____

Thoughts & Prayer:

_____
_____
_____
_____
_____
_____
_____
_____

Today's Entry

Date:_____   Exercise:_____   Water Intake: (1)(2)(3)(4)(5)(6)(7)(8)

5 Things I'm Thankful For:

1._____
2._____
3._____
4._____
5._____

My Quote Of The Day:

Today's Bible Reading (References & Notes):

_____
_____
_____

Prayer Requests/BIG Dreams:

_____
_____
_____

How I'm Feeling Today (Circle All That Apply):

* Happy * Stressed/Anxious * Peaceful * Tired
*Thankful * Sad * Angry *Lonely * Relieved
* Other:

Answers To Prayer:

_____
_____
_____

What's Bothering Me:

_____
_____

How I Can Resolve It (Or Pray About It):

_____
_____

Thoughts & Prayer:

_____
_____
_____
_____
_____
_____
_____
_____

Today's Entry

Date:_____ Exercise:_____ Water Intake: (1)(2)(3)(4)(5)(6)(7)(8)

5 Things I'm Thankful For:

1._____
2._____
3._____
4._____
5._____

My Quote Of The Day:

Today's Bible Reading (References & Notes):

_____
_____
_____
_____

Prayer Requests/BIG Dreams:

_____
_____
_____
_____

How I'm Feeling Today (Circle All That Apply):

* Happy * Stressed/Anxious * Peaceful * Tired
*Thankful * Sad * Angry *Lonely * Relieved
* Other:

Answers To Prayer:

_____
_____
_____

What's Bothering Me:

_____
_____

How I Can Resolve It (Or Pray About It):

_____
_____

Thoughts & Prayer:

_____
_____
_____
_____
_____
_____
_____
_____
_____

Today's Entry

Date:_____   Exercise:_____   Water Intake: (1)(2)(3)(4)(5)(6)(7)(8)

5 Things I'm Thankful For:

1._____
2._____
3._____
4._____
5._____

My Quote Of The Day:

Today's Bible Reading (References & Notes):

_____
_____
_____

Prayer Requests/BIG Dreams:

_____
_____
_____

How I'm Feeling Today (Circle All That Apply):

* Happy * Stressed/Anxious * Peaceful * Tired
*Thankful * Sad * Angry *Lonely * Relieved
* Other:

Answers To Prayer:

_____
_____

What's Bothering Me:

_____
_____

How I Can Resolve It (Or Pray About It):

_____
_____

Thoughts & Prayer:

_____
_____
_____
_____
_____
_____
_____

Today's Entry

Date:_____   Exercise:_____   Water Intake: (1)(2)(3)(4)(5)(6)(7)(8)

5 Things I'm Thankful For:

1._____
2._____
3._____
4._____
5._____

My Quote Of The Day:

Today's Bible Reading (References & Notes):

_____
_____
_____

Prayer Requests/BIG Dreams:

_____
_____
_____

How I'm Feeling Today (Circle All That Apply):

* Happy * Stressed/Anxious * Peaceful * Tired
*Thankful * Sad * Angry *Lonely * Relieved
* Other:

Answers To Prayer:

_____
_____
_____

What's Bothering Me:

_____
_____

How I Can Resolve It (Or Pray About It):

_____
_____

Thoughts & Prayer:

_____
_____
_____
_____
_____
_____
_____
_____

Today's Entry

Date:_____   Exercise:_____   Water Intake: (1)(2)(3)(4)(5)(6)(7)(8)

5 Things I'm Thankful For:

1._____
2._____
3._____
4._____
5._____

My Quote Of The Day:

Today's Bible Reading (References & Notes):

_____
_____
_____

Prayer Requests/BIG Dreams:

_____
_____
_____

How I'm Feeling Today (Circle All That Apply):

* Happy * Stressed/Anxious * Peaceful * Tired
*Thankful * Sad * Angry *Lonely * Relieved
* Other:

Answers To Prayer:

_____
_____
_____

What's Bothering Me:

_____
_____

How I Can Resolve It (Or Pray About It):

_____
_____

Thoughts & Prayer:

_____
_____
_____
_____
_____
_____
_____
_____

Today's Entry

Date:_____   Exercise:_____   Water Intake: (1)(2)(3)(4)(5)(6)(7)(8)

5 Things I'm Thankful For:

1._____
2._____
3._____
4._____
5._____

My Quote Of The Day:

Today's Bible Reading (References & Notes):

_____
_____
_____

Prayer Requests/BIG Dreams:

_____
_____
_____

How I'm Feeling Today (Circle All That Apply):

* Happy * Stressed/Anxious * Peaceful * Tired
*Thankful * Sad * Angry *Lonely * Relieved
* Other:

Answers To Prayer:

_____
_____
_____

What's Bothering Me:

_____
_____

How I Can Resolve It (Or Pray About It):

_____
_____

Thoughts & Prayer:

_____
_____
_____
_____
_____
_____
_____
_____

Today's Entry

Date:_____ Exercise:_____ Water Intake: (1)(2)(3)(4)(5)(6)(7)(8)

5 Things I'm Thankful For:

1._____
2._____
3._____
4._____
5._____

My Quote Of The Day:

Today's Bible Reading (References & Notes):

_____
_____
_____

Prayer Requests/BIG Dreams:

_____
_____
_____

How I'm Feeling Today (Circle All That Apply):

* Happy * Stressed/Anxious * Peaceful * Tired
*Thankful * Sad * Angry *Lonely * Relieved
* Other:

Answers To Prayer:

_____
_____
_____

What's Bothering Me:

_____
_____

How I Can Resolve It (Or Pray About It):

_____
_____

Thoughts & Prayer:

_____
_____
_____
_____
_____
_____
_____
_____

Today's Entry

Date:_____ Exercise:_____ Water Intake: (1)(2)(3)(4)(5)(6)(7)(8)

5 Things I'm Thankful For:

1._____
2._____
3._____
4._____
5._____

My Quote Of The Day:

Today's Bible Reading (References & Notes):

_____
_____
_____
_____

Prayer Requests/BIG Dreams:

_____
_____
_____

How I'm Feeling Today (Circle All That Apply):

* Happy * Stressed/Anxious * Peaceful * Tired
*Thankful * Sad * Angry *Lonely * Relieved
* Other:

Answers To Prayer:

_____
_____
_____

What's Bothering Me:

_____
_____

How I Can Resolve It (Or Pray About It):

_____
_____

Thoughts & Prayer:

_____
_____
_____
_____
_____
_____
_____
_____

Today's Entry

Date:_____   Exercise:_____   Water Intake: (1)(2)(3)(4)(5)(6)(7)(8)

5 Things I'm Thankful For:

1._____
2._____
3._____
4._____
5._____

My Quote Of The Day:

Today's Bible Reading (References & Notes):

_____
_____
_____

Prayer Requests/BIG Dreams:

_____
_____
_____

How I'm Feeling Today (Circle All That Apply):

* Happy * Stressed/Anxious * Peaceful * Tired
*Thankful * Sad * Angry *Lonely * Relieved
* Other:

Answers To Prayer:

_____
_____
_____

What's Bothering Me:

_____
_____

How I Can Resolve It (Or Pray About It):

_____
_____

Thoughts & Prayer:

_____
_____
_____
_____
_____
_____
_____
_____

Today's Entry

Date:_____   Exercise:_____   Water Intake: (1)(2)(3)(4)(5)(6)(7)(8)

5 Things I'm Thankful For:

1._____
2._____
3._____
4._____
5._____

My Quote Of The Day:

Today's Bible Reading (References & Notes):

_____
_____
_____

Prayer Requests/BIG Dreams:

_____
_____
_____

How I'm Feeling Today (Circle All That Apply):

* Happy * Stressed/Anxious * Peaceful * Tired
*Thankful * Sad * Angry *Lonely * Relieved
* Other:

Answers To Prayer:

_____
_____
_____

What's Bothering Me:

_____
_____

How I Can Resolve It (Or Pray About It):

_____
_____

Thoughts & Prayer:

_____
_____
_____
_____
_____
_____
_____
_____

Today's Entry

Date:_____   Exercise:_____   Water Intake: (1)(2)(3)(4)(5)(6)(7)(8)

5 Things I'm Thankful For:

1._____
2._____
3._____
4._____
5._____

My Quote Of The Day:

Today's Bible Reading (References & Notes):

_____
_____
_____

Prayer Requests/BIG Dreams:

_____
_____
_____

How I'm Feeling Today (Circle All That Apply):

* Happy * Stressed/Anxious * Peaceful * Tired
*Thankful * Sad * Angry *Lonely * Relieved
* Other:

Answers To Prayer:

_____
_____
_____

What's Bothering Me:

_____
_____

How I Can Resolve It (Or Pray About It):

_____
_____

Thoughts & Prayer:

_____
_____
_____
_____
_____
_____
_____
_____
_____

Today's Entry

Date:_____   Exercise:_____   Water Intake: (1)(2)(3)(4)(5)(6)(7)(8)

5 Things I'm Thankful For:

1._____
2._____
3._____
4._____
5._____

My Quote Of The Day:

Today's Bible Reading (References & Notes):

_____
_____
_____

Prayer Requests/BIG Dreams:

_____
_____
_____

How I'm Feeling Today (Circle All That Apply):

* Happy * Stressed/Anxious * Peaceful * Tired
*Thankful * Sad * Angry *Lonely * Relieved
* Other:

Answers To Prayer:

_____
_____
_____

What's Bothering Me:

_____
_____

How I Can Resolve It (Or Pray About It):

_____
_____

Thoughts & Prayer:

_____
_____
_____
_____
_____
_____
_____
_____

Today's Entry

Date:_____   Exercise:_____   Water Intake: (1)(2)(3)(4)(5)(6)(7)(8)

5 Things I'm Thankful For:

1._____
2._____
3._____
4._____
5._____

My Quote Of The Day:

Today's Bible Reading (References & Notes):

_____
_____
_____

Prayer Requests/BIG Dreams:

_____
_____
_____

How I'm Feeling Today (Circle All That Apply):

* Happy * Stressed/Anxious * Peaceful * Tired
*Thankful * Sad * Angry *Lonely * Relieved
* Other:

Answers To Prayer:

_____
_____
_____

What's Bothering Me:

_____
_____

How I Can Resolve It (Or Pray About It):

_____
_____

Thoughts & Prayer:

_____
_____
_____
_____
_____
_____
_____
_____

Today's Entry

Date:_____ Exercise:_____ Water Intake: (1)(2)(3)(4)(5)(6)(7)(8)

5 Things I'm Thankful For:

1._____
2._____
3._____
4._____
5._____

My Quote Of The Day:

Today's Bible Reading (References & Notes):

_____
_____
_____

Prayer Requests/BIG Dreams:

_____
_____
_____

How I'm Feeling Today (Circle All That Apply):

* Happy * Stressed/Anxious * Peaceful * Tired
*Thankful * Sad * Angry *Lonely * Relieved
* Other:

Answers To Prayer:

_____
_____
_____

What's Bothering Me:

_____
_____

How I Can Resolve It (Or Pray About It):

_____
_____

Thoughts & Prayer:

_____
_____
_____
_____
_____
_____
_____
_____

Today's Entry

Date:_____   Exercise:_____   Water Intake: (1)(2)(3)(4)(5)(6)(7)(8)

5 Things I'm Thankful For:

1._____
2._____
3._____
4._____
5._____

My Quote Of The Day:

Today's Bible Reading (References & Notes):

_____
_____
_____
_____

Prayer Requests/BIG Dreams:

_____
_____
_____

How I'm Feeling Today (Circle All That Apply):

* Happy * Stressed/Anxious * Peaceful * Tired
*Thankful * Sad * Angry *Lonely * Relieved
* Other:

Answers To Prayer:

_____
_____
_____

What's Bothering Me:

_____
_____

How I Can Resolve It (Or Pray About It):

_____
_____

Thoughts & Prayer:

_____
_____
_____
_____
_____
_____
_____
_____

Today's Entry

Date:_____   Exercise:_____   Water Intake: (1)(2)(3)(4)(5)(6)(7)(8)

5 Things I'm Thankful For:

1._____
2._____
3._____
4._____
5._____

My Quote Of The Day:

Today's Bible Reading (References & Notes):

_____
_____
_____

Prayer Requests/BIG Dreams:

_____
_____
_____

How I'm Feeling Today (Circle All That Apply):

* Happy * Stressed/Anxious * Peaceful * Tired
*Thankful * Sad * Angry *Lonely * Relieved
* Other:

Answers To Prayer:

_____
_____
_____

What's Bothering Me:

_____
_____

How I Can Resolve It (Or Pray About It):

_____
_____

Thoughts & Prayer:

_____
_____
_____
_____
_____
_____
_____

Today's Entry

Date:_____   Exercise:_____   Water Intake: (1)(2)(3)(4)(5)(6)(7)(8)

5 Things I'm Thankful For:

1._____
2._____
3._____
4._____
5._____

My Quote Of The Day:

Today's Bible Reading (References & Notes):

_____
_____
_____

Prayer Requests/BIG Dreams:

_____
_____
_____

How I'm Feeling Today (Circle All That Apply):

* Happy * Stressed/Anxious * Peaceful * Tired
*Thankful * Sad * Angry *Lonely * Relieved
* Other:

Answers To Prayer:

_____
_____
_____

What's Bothering Me:

_____
_____

How I Can Resolve It (Or Pray About It):

_____
_____

Thoughts & Prayer:

_____
_____
_____
_____
_____
_____
_____
_____

Today's Entry

Date:_____   Exercise:_____   Water Intake: (1)(2)(3)(4)(5)(6)(7)(8)

5 Things I'm Thankful For:

1._____
2._____
3._____
4._____
5._____

My Quote Of The Day:

Today's Bible Reading (References & Notes):

_____
_____
_____

Prayer Requests/BIG Dreams:

_____
_____
_____

How I'm Feeling Today (Circle All That Apply):

* Happy * Stressed/Anxious * Peaceful * Tired
*Thankful * Sad * Angry *Lonely * Relieved
* Other:

Answers To Prayer:

_____
_____
_____

What's Bothering Me:

_____
_____

How I Can Resolve It (Or Pray About It):

_____
_____
_____

Thoughts & Prayer:

_____
_____
_____
_____
_____
_____
_____
_____

Today's Entry

Date:_____ Exercise:_____ Water Intake: (1)(2)(3)(4)(5)(6)(7)(8)

5 Things I'm Thankful For:

1._____
2._____
3._____
4._____
5._____

My Quote Of The Day:

Today's Bible Reading (References & Notes):

_____
_____
_____

Prayer Requests/BIG Dreams:

_____
_____
_____

How I'm Feeling Today (Circle All That Apply):

* Happy * Stressed/Anxious * Peaceful * Tired
*Thankful * Sad * Angry *Lonely * Relieved
* Other:

Answers To Prayer:

_____
_____
_____

What's Bothering Me:

_____
_____

How I Can Resolve It (Or Pray About It):

_____
_____

Thoughts & Prayer:

_____
_____
_____
_____
_____
_____
_____
_____

Today's Entry

Date:_____   Exercise:_____   Water Intake: (1)(2)(3)(4)(5)(6)(7)(8)

5 Things I'm Thankful For:

1._____
2._____
3._____
4._____
5._____

My Quote Of The Day:

Today's Bible Reading (References & Notes):

_____
_____
_____

Prayer Requests/BIG Dreams:

_____
_____
_____

How I'm Feeling Today (Circle All That Apply):

* Happy * Stressed/Anxious * Peaceful * Tired
*Thankful * Sad * Angry *Lonely * Relieved
* Other:

Answers To Prayer:

_____
_____
_____

What's Bothering Me:

_____
_____

How I Can Resolve It (Or Pray About It):

_____
_____

Thoughts & Prayer:

_____
_____
_____
_____
_____
_____
_____

Today's Entry

Date:_____   Exercise:_____   Water Intake: (1)(2)(3)(4)(5)(6)(7)(8)

5 Things I'm Thankful For:

1._____
2._____
3._____
4._____
5._____

My Quote Of The Day:

Today's Bible Reading (References & Notes):

_____
_____
_____

Prayer Requests/BIG Dreams:

_____
_____
_____

How I'm Feeling Today (Circle All That Apply):

* Happy * Stressed/Anxious * Peaceful * Tired
*Thankful * Sad * Angry *Lonely * Relieved
* Other:

Answers To Prayer:

_____
_____
_____

What's Bothering Me:

_____
_____

How I Can Resolve It (Or Pray About It):

_____
_____

Thoughts & Prayer:

_____
_____
_____
_____
_____
_____
_____
_____
_____

Today's Entry

Date:_____ Exercise:_____ Water Intake: (1)(2)(3)(4)(5)(6)(7)(8)

5 Things I'm Thankful For:

1._____
2._____
3._____
4._____
5._____

My Quote Of The Day:

Today's Bible Reading (References & Notes):

_____
_____
_____

Prayer Requests/BIG Dreams:

_____
_____
_____

How I'm Feeling Today (Circle All That Apply):

* Happy * Stressed/Anxious * Peaceful * Tired
*Thankful * Sad * Angry *Lonely * Relieved
* Other:

Answers To Prayer:

_____
_____
_____

What's Bothering Me:

_____
_____

How I Can Resolve It (Or Pray About It):

_____
_____

Thoughts & Prayer:

_____
_____
_____
_____
_____
_____
_____
_____

"You will seek me
and find me when you
seek me with all your
heart."
(Jer. 29:13)

Today's Entry

Date:_____   Exercise:_____   Water Intake: (1)(2)(3)(4)(5)(6)(7)(8)

5 Things I'm Thankful For:

1._____
2._____
3._____
4._____
5._____

My Quote Of The Day:

Today's Bible Reading (References & Notes):

_____
_____
_____

Prayer Requests/BIG Dreams:

_____
_____
_____

How I'm Feeling Today (Circle All That Apply):

* Happy * Stressed/Anxious * Peaceful * Tired
*Thankful * Sad * Angry *Lonely * Relieved
* Other:

Answers To Prayer:

_____
_____
_____

What's Bothering Me:

_____
_____

How I Can Resolve It (Or Pray About It):

_____
_____

Thoughts & Prayer:

_____
_____
_____
_____
_____
_____
_____

Today's Entry

Date:_____ Exercise:_____ Water Intake: (1)(2)(3)(4)(5)(6)(7)(8)

5 Things I'm Thankful For:

1._____
2._____
3._____
4._____
5._____

My Quote Of The Day:

Today's Bible Reading (References & Notes):

_____
_____
_____
_____

Prayer Requests/BIG Dreams:

_____
_____
_____
_____

How I'm Feeling Today (Circle All That Apply):

* Happy * Stressed/Anxious * Peaceful * Tired
*Thankful * Sad * Angry *Lonely * Relieved
* Other:

Answers To Prayer:

_____
_____
_____

What's Bothering Me:

_____
_____

How I Can Resolve It (Or Pray About It):

_____
_____

Thoughts & Prayer:

_____
_____
_____
_____
_____
_____
_____
_____

Today's Entry

Date:_____   Exercise:_____   Water Intake: (1)(2)(3)(4)(5)(6)(7)(8)

5 Things I'm Thankful For:

1._____
2._____
3._____
4._____
5._____

My Quote Of The Day:

Today's Bible Reading (References & Notes):

_____
_____
_____

Prayer Requests/BIG Dreams:

_____
_____
_____

How I'm Feeling Today (Circle All That Apply):

* Happy * Stressed/Anxious * Peaceful * Tired
*Thankful * Sad * Angry *Lonely * Relieved
* Other:

Answers To Prayer:

_____
_____
_____

What's Bothering Me:

_____
_____

How I Can Resolve It (Or Pray About It):

_____
_____

Thoughts & Prayer:

_____
_____
_____
_____
_____
_____
_____
_____

Today's Entry

Date:_____ Exercise:_____ Water Intake: (1)(2)(3)(4)(5)(6)(7)(8)

5 Things I'm Thankful For:

1._____
2._____
3._____
4._____
5._____

My Quote Of The Day:

Today's Bible Reading (References & Notes):

_____
_____
_____

Prayer Requests/BIG Dreams:

_____
_____
_____

How I'm Feeling Today (Circle All That Apply):

* Happy * Stressed/Anxious * Peaceful * Tired
*Thankful * Sad * Angry *Lonely * Relieved
* Other:

Answers To Prayer:

_____
_____
_____

What's Bothering Me:

_____
_____

How I Can Resolve It (Or Pray About It):

_____
_____

Thoughts & Prayer:

_____
_____
_____
_____
_____
_____
_____
_____

Today's Entry

Date:_____ Exercise:_____ Water Intake: (1)(2)(3)(4)(5)(6)(7)(8)

5 Things I'm Thankful For:

1._____
2._____
3._____
4._____
5._____

My Quote Of The Day:

Today's Bible Reading (References & Notes):

_____
_____
_____

Prayer Requests/BIG Dreams:

_____
_____
_____
_____

How I'm Feeling Today (Circle All That Apply):

* Happy * Stressed/Anxious * Peaceful * Tired
*Thankful * Sad * Angry *Lonely * Relieved
* Other:

Answers To Prayer:

_____
_____
_____

What's Bothering Me:

_____
_____

How I Can Resolve It (Or Pray About It):

_____
_____

Thoughts & Prayer:

_____
_____
_____
_____
_____
_____
_____
_____

Today's Entry

Date:_____ Exercise:_____ Water Intake: (1)(2)(3)(4)(5)(6)(7)(8)

5 Things I'm Thankful For:

1._____
2._____
3._____
4._____
5._____

My Quote Of The Day:

Today's Bible Reading (References & Notes):

_____
_____
_____

Prayer Requests/BIG Dreams:

_____
_____
_____

How I'm Feeling Today (Circle All That Apply):

* Happy * Stressed/Anxious * Peaceful * Tired
*Thankful * Sad * Angry *Lonely * Relieved
* Other:

Answers To Prayer:

_____
_____
_____

What's Bothering Me:

_____
_____

How I Can Resolve It (Or Pray About It):

_____
_____

Thoughts & Prayer:

_____
_____
_____
_____
_____
_____
_____
_____

Today's Entry

Date:_____ Exercise:_____ Water Intake: (1)(2)(3)(4)(5)(6)(7)(8)

5 Things I'm Thankful For:

1._____
2._____
3._____
4._____
5._____

My Quote Of The Day:

Today's Bible Reading (References & Notes):

_____
_____
_____

Prayer Requests/BIG Dreams:

_____
_____
_____

How I'm Feeling Today (Circle All That Apply):

* Happy * Stressed/Anxious * Peaceful * Tired
*Thankful * Sad * Angry *Lonely * Relieved
* Other:

Answers To Prayer:

_____
_____
_____

What's Bothering Me:

_____
_____

How I Can Resolve It (Or Pray About It):

_____
_____

Thoughts & Prayer:

_____
_____
_____
_____
_____
_____
_____
_____

Today's Entry

Date:_____ Exercise:_____ Water Intake: (1)(2)(3)(4)(5)(6)(7)(8)

5 Things I'm Thankful For:

1._____
2._____
3._____
4._____
5._____

My Quote Of The Day:

Today's Bible Reading (References & Notes):

_____
_____
_____

Prayer Requests/BIG Dreams:

_____
_____
_____

How I'm Feeling Today (Circle All That Apply):

* Happy * Stressed/Anxious * Peaceful * Tired
*Thankful * Sad * Angry *Lonely * Relieved
* Other:

Answers To Prayer:

_____
_____
_____

What's Bothering Me:

_____
_____

How I Can Resolve It (Or Pray About It):

_____
_____

Thoughts & Prayer:

_____
_____
_____
_____
_____
_____
_____
_____

Today's Entry

Date:_____   Exercise:_____   Water Intake: (1)(2)(3)(4)(5)(6)(7)(8)

5 Things I'm Thankful For:

1._____
2._____
3._____
4._____
5._____

My Quote Of The Day:

Today's Bible Reading (References & Notes):

_____
_____
_____
_____

Prayer Requests/BIG Dreams:

_____
_____
_____
_____

How I'm Feeling Today (Circle All That Apply):

* Happy * Stressed/Anxious * Peaceful * Tired
*Thankful * Sad * Angry *Lonely * Relieved
* Other:

Answers To Prayer:

_____
_____
_____

What's Bothering Me:

_____
_____

How I Can Resolve It (Or Pray About It):

_____
_____

Thoughts & Prayer:

_____
_____
_____
_____
_____
_____
_____
_____

Today's Entry

Date:_____   Exercise:_____   Water Intake: (1)(2)(3)(4)(5)(6)(7)(8)

5 Things I'm Thankful For:

1._____
2._____
3._____
4._____
5._____

My Quote Of The Day:

Today's Bible Reading (References & Notes):

_____
_____
_____

Prayer Requests/BIG Dreams:

_____
_____
_____

How I'm Feeling Today (Circle All That Apply):

* Happy * Stressed/Anxious * Peaceful * Tired
*Thankful * Sad * Angry *Lonely * Relieved
* Other:

Answers To Prayer:

_____
_____
_____

What's Bothering Me:

_____
_____

How I Can Resolve It (Or Pray About It):

_____
_____

Thoughts & Prayer:

_____
_____
_____
_____
_____
_____
_____
_____

Today's Entry

Date:_____   Exercise:_____   Water Intake: (1)(2)(3)(4)(5)(6)(7)(8)

5 Things I'm Thankful For:

1._____
2._____
3._____
4._____
5._____

My Quote Of The Day:

Today's Bible Reading (References & Notes):

_____
_____
_____

Prayer Requests/BIG Dreams:

_____
_____
_____

How I'm Feeling Today (Circle All That Apply):

* Happy * Stressed/Anxious * Peaceful * Tired
*Thankful * Sad * Angry *Lonely * Relieved
* Other:

Answers To Prayer:

_____
_____
_____

What's Bothering Me:

_____
_____

How I Can Resolve It (Or Pray About It):

_____
_____

Thoughts & Prayer:

_____
_____
_____
_____
_____
_____
_____
_____

Today's Entry

Date:_____ Exercise:_____ Water Intake: (1)(2)(3)(4)(5)(6)(7)(8)

5 Things I'm Thankful For:

1._____
2._____
3._____
4._____
5._____

My Quote Of The Day:

Today's Bible Reading (References & Notes):

_____
_____
_____

Prayer Requests/BIG Dreams:

_____
_____
_____

How I'm Feeling Today (Circle All That Apply):

* Happy * Stressed/Anxious * Peaceful * Tired
*Thankful * Sad * Angry *Lonely * Relieved
* Other:

Answers To Prayer:

_____
_____
_____

What's Bothering Me:

_____
_____

How I Can Resolve It (Or Pray About It):

_____
_____

Thoughts & Prayer:

_____
_____
_____
_____
_____
_____
_____
_____

Today's Entry

Date:_____ Exercise:_____ Water Intake: (1)(2)(3)(4)(5)(6)(7)(8)

5 Things I'm Thankful For:

1._____
2._____
3._____
4._____
5._____

My Quote Of The Day:

Today's Bible Reading (References & Notes):

_____
_____
_____

Prayer Requests/BIG Dreams:

_____
_____
_____

How I'm Feeling Today (Circle All That Apply):

* Happy * Stressed/Anxious * Peaceful * Tired
*Thankful * Sad * Angry *Lonely * Relieved
* Other:

Answers To Prayer:

_____
_____
_____

What's Bothering Me:

_____
_____

How I Can Resolve It (Or Pray About It):

_____
_____

Thoughts & Prayer:

_____
_____
_____
_____
_____
_____
_____
_____

Today's Entry

*Date:*_____ *Exercise:*_____ *Water Intake: (1)(2)(3)(4)(5)(6)(7)(8)*

5 Things I'm Thankful For:

1._____
2._____
3._____
4._____
5._____

My Quote Of The Day:

Today's Bible Reading (References & Notes):

_____
_____
_____

Prayer Requests/BIG Dreams:

_____
_____
_____

How I'm Feeling Today (Circle All That Apply):

* Happy * Stressed/Anxious * Peaceful * Tired
*Thankful * Sad * Angry *Lonely * Relieved
* Other:

Answers To Prayer:

_____
_____
_____

What's Bothering Me:

_____
_____

How I Can Resolve It (Or Pray About It):

_____
_____

Thoughts & Prayer:

_____
_____
_____
_____
_____
_____
_____
_____
_____

Today's Entry

Date:_____   Exercise:_____   Water Intake: (1)(2)(3)(4)(5)(6)(7)(8)

5 Things I'm Thankful For:

1._____
2._____
3._____
4._____
5._____

My Quote Of The Day:

Today's Bible Reading (References & Notes):

_____
_____
_____

Prayer Requests/BIG Dreams:

_____
_____
_____

How I'm Feeling Today (Circle All That Apply):

* Happy * Stressed/Anxious * Peaceful * Tired
*Thankful * Sad * Angry *Lonely * Relieved
* Other:

Answers To Prayer:

_____
_____
_____

What's Bothering Me:

_____
_____

How I Can Resolve It (Or Pray About It):

_____
_____

Thoughts & Prayer:

_____
_____
_____
_____
_____
_____
_____
_____

Today's Entry

Date:_____ Exercise:_____ Water Intake: (1)(2)(3)(4)(5)(6)(7)(8)

5 Things I'm Thankful For:

1._____
2._____
3._____
4._____
5._____

My Quote Of The Day:

Today's Bible Reading (References & Notes):

_____
_____
_____

Prayer Requests/BIG Dreams:

_____
_____
_____

How I'm Feeling Today (Circle All That Apply):

* Happy * Stressed/Anxious * Peaceful * Tired
*Thankful * Sad * Angry *Lonely * Relieved
* Other:

Answers To Prayer:

_____
_____
_____

What's Bothering Me:

_____
_____

How I Can Resolve It (Or Pray About It):

_____
_____

Thoughts & Prayer:

_____
_____
_____
_____
_____
_____
_____
_____

Today's Entry

Date:_____ Exercise:_____ Water Intake: (1)(2)(3)(4)(5)(6)(7)(8)

5 Things I'm Thankful For:

1._____
2._____
3._____
4._____
5._____

My Quote Of The Day:

Today's Bible Reading (References & Notes):

_____
_____
_____
_____

Prayer Requests/BIG Dreams:

_____
_____
_____

How I'm Feeling Today (Circle All That Apply):

* Happy * Stressed/Anxious * Peaceful * Tired
*Thankful * Sad * Angry *Lonely * Relieved
* Other:

Answers To Prayer:

_____
_____

What's Bothering Me:

_____
_____

How I Can Resolve It (Or Pray About It):

_____
_____

Thoughts & Prayer:

_____
_____
_____
_____
_____
_____
_____
_____

Today's Entry

Date:_____   Exercise:_____   Water Intake: (1)(2)(3)(4)(5)(6)(7)(8)

5 Things I'm Thankful For:

1._____
2._____
3._____
4._____
5._____

My Quote Of The Day:

Today's Bible Reading (References & Notes):

_____
_____
_____

Prayer Requests/BIG Dreams:

_____
_____
_____

How I'm Feeling Today (Circle All That Apply):

* Happy * Stressed/Anxious * Peaceful * Tired
*Thankful * Sad * Angry *Lonely * Relieved
* Other:

Answers To Prayer:

_____
_____
_____

What's Bothering Me:

_____
_____

How I Can Resolve It (Or Pray About It):

_____
_____

Thoughts & Prayer:

_____
_____
_____
_____
_____
_____
_____
_____

Today's Entry

Date:_____   Exercise:_____   Water Intake: (1)(2)(3)(4)(5)(6)(7)(8)

5 Things I'm Thankful For:

1._____
2._____
3._____
4._____
5._____

My Quote Of The Day:

Today's Bible Reading (References & Notes):

_____
_____
_____
_____

Prayer Requests/BIG Dreams:

_____
_____
_____

How I'm Feeling Today (Circle All That Apply):

* Happy * Stressed/Anxious * Peaceful * Tired
*Thankful * Sad * Angry *Lonely * Relieved
* Other:

Answers To Prayer:

_____
_____
_____

What's Bothering Me:

_____
_____

How I Can Resolve It (Or Pray About It):

_____
_____

Thoughts & Prayer:

_____
_____
_____
_____
_____
_____
_____
_____

Today's Entry

Date:_____ Exercise:_____ Water Intake: (1)(2)(3)(4)(5)(6)(7)(8)

5 Things I'm Thankful For:

1._____
2._____
3._____
4._____
5._____

My Quote Of The Day:

Today's Bible Reading (References & Notes):

_____
_____
_____

Prayer Requests/BIG Dreams:

_____
_____
_____

How I'm Feeling Today (Circle All That Apply):

* Happy * Stressed/Anxious * Peaceful * Tired
*Thankful * Sad * Angry *Lonely * Relieved
* Other:

Answers To Prayer:

_____
_____
_____

What's Bothering Me:

_____
_____

How I Can Resolve It (Or Pray About It):

_____
_____

Thoughts & Prayer:

_____
_____
_____
_____
_____
_____
_____
_____

Today's Entry

Date:_____   Exercise:_____   Water Intake: (1)(2)(3)(4)(5)(6)(7)(8)

5 Things I'm Thankful For:

1._____
2._____
3._____
4._____
5._____

My Quote Of The Day:

Today's Bible Reading (References & Notes):

_____
_____
_____

Prayer Requests/BIG Dreams:

_____
_____
_____
_____

How I'm Feeling Today (Circle All That Apply):

* Happy * Stressed/Anxious * Peaceful * Tired
*Thankful * Sad * Angry *Lonely * Relieved
* Other:

Answers To Prayer:

_____
_____
_____

What's Bothering Me:

_____
_____

How I Can Resolve It (Or Pray About It):

_____
_____

Thoughts & Prayer:

_____
_____
_____
_____
_____
_____
_____
_____

Today's Entry

Date:_____   Exercise:_____   Water Intake: (1)(2)(3)(4)(5)(6)(7)(8)

5 Things I'm Thankful For:

1._____
2._____
3._____
4._____
5._____

My Quote Of The Day:

Today's Bible Reading (References & Notes):

_____
_____
_____

Prayer Requests/BIG Dreams:

_____
_____
_____

How I'm Feeling Today (Circle All That Apply):

* Happy * Stressed/Anxious * Peaceful * Tired
*Thankful * Sad * Angry *Lonely * Relieved
* Other:

Answers To Prayer:

_____
_____
_____

What's Bothering Me:

_____
_____

How I Can Resolve It (Or Pray About It):

_____
_____

Thoughts & Prayer:

_____
_____
_____
_____
_____
_____
_____
_____

Today's Entry

Date:_____   Exercise:_____   Water Intake: (1)(2)(3)(4)(5)(6)(7)(8)

5 Things I'm Thankful For:

1._____
2._____
3._____
4._____
5._____

My Quote Of The Day:

Today's Bible Reading (References & Notes):

_____
_____
_____
_____

Prayer Requests/BIG Dreams:

_____
_____
_____

How I'm Feeling Today (Circle All That Apply):

* Happy * Stressed/Anxious * Peaceful * Tired
*Thankful * Sad * Angry *Lonely * Relieved
* Other:

Answers To Prayer:

_____
_____
_____

What's Bothering Me:

_____
_____

How I Can Resolve It (Or Pray About It):

_____
_____

Thoughts & Prayer:

_____
_____
_____
_____
_____
_____
_____
_____

Today's Entry

Date:_____ Exercise:_____ Water Intake: (1)(2)(3)(4)(5)(6)(7)(8)

5 Things I'm Thankful For:

1._____
2._____
3._____
4._____
5._____

My Quote Of The Day:

Today's Bible Reading (References & Notes):

_____
_____
_____

Prayer Requests/BIG Dreams:

_____
_____
_____

How I'm Feeling Today (Circle All That Apply):

* Happy * Stressed/Anxious * Peaceful * Tired
*Thankful * Sad * Angry *Lonely * Relieved
* Other:

Answers To Prayer:

_____
_____
_____

What's Bothering Me:

_____
_____

How I Can Resolve It (Or Pray About It):

_____
_____

Thoughts & Prayer:

_____
_____
_____
_____
_____
_____
_____
_____

Today's Entry

Date:_____   Exercise:_____   Water Intake: (1)(2)(3)(4)(5)(6)(7)(8)

5 Things I'm Thankful For:

1._____
2._____
3._____
4._____
5._____

My Quote Of The Day:

Today's Bible Reading (References & Notes):

_____
_____
_____

Prayer Requests/BIG Dreams:

_____
_____
_____

How I'm Feeling Today (Circle All That Apply):

* Happy * Stressed/Anxious * Peaceful * Tired
*Thankful * Sad * Angry *Lonely * Relieved
* Other:

Answers To Prayer:

_____
_____
_____

What's Bothering Me:

_____
_____

How I Can Resolve It (Or Pray About It):

_____
_____

Thoughts & Prayer:

_____
_____
_____
_____
_____
_____
_____

Today's Entry

Date:_____   Exercise:_____   Water Intake: (1)(2)(3)(4)(5)(6)(7)(8)

5 Things I'm Thankful For:

1._____
2._____
3._____
4._____
5._____

My Quote Of The Day:

Today's Bible Reading (References & Notes):

_____
_____
_____
_____

Prayer Requests/BIG Dreams:

_____
_____
_____
_____

How I'm Feeling Today (Circle All That Apply):

* Happy * Stressed/Anxious * Peaceful * Tired
*Thankful * Sad * Angry *Lonely * Relieved
* Other:

Answers To Prayer:

_____
_____
_____

What's Bothering Me:

_____
_____

How I Can Resolve It (Or Pray About It):

_____
_____

Thoughts & Prayer:

_____
_____
_____
_____
_____
_____
_____
_____
_____

Today's Entry

Date:_____ Exercise:_____ Water Intake: (1)(2)(3)(4)(5)(6)(7)(8)

5 Things I'm Thankful For:

1._____
2._____
3._____
4._____
5._____

My Quote Of The Day:

Today's Bible Reading (References & Notes):

_____
_____
_____
_____

Prayer Requests/BIG Dreams:

_____
_____
_____
_____

How I'm Feeling Today (Circle All That Apply):

* Happy * Stressed/Anxious * Peaceful * Tired
*Thankful * Sad * Angry *Lonely * Relieved
* Other:

Answers To Prayer:

_____
_____
_____

What's Bothering Me:

_____
_____

How I Can Resolve It (Or Pray About It):

_____
_____

Thoughts & Prayer:

_____
_____
_____
_____
_____
_____
_____
_____

Today's Entry

Date:_____   Exercise:_____   Water Intake: (1)(2)(3)(4)(5)(6)(7)(8)

5 Things I'm Thankful For:

1._____
2._____
3._____
4._____
5._____

My Quote Of The Day:

Today's Bible Reading (References & Notes):

_____
_____
_____

Prayer Requests/BIG Dreams:

_____
_____
_____

How I'm Feeling Today (Circle All That Apply):

* Happy * Stressed/Anxious * Peaceful * Tired
*Thankful * Sad * Angry *Lonely * Relieved
* Other:

Answers To Prayer:

_____
_____
_____

What's Bothering Me:

_____
_____

How I Can Resolve It (Or Pray About It):

_____
_____

Thoughts & Prayer:

_____
_____
_____
_____
_____
_____
_____
_____

Today's Entry

Date:_____ Exercise:_____ Water Intake: (1)(2)(3)(4)(5)(6)(7)(8)

5 Things I'm Thankful For:

1._____
2._____
3._____
4._____
5._____

My Quote Of The Day:

Today's Bible Reading (References & Notes):

_____
_____
_____

Prayer Requests/BIG Dreams:

_____
_____
_____

How I'm Feeling Today (Circle All That Apply):

* Happy * Stressed/Anxious * Peaceful * Tired
*Thankful * Sad * Angry *Lonely * Relieved
* Other:

Answers To Prayer:

_____
_____
_____

What's Bothering Me:

_____
_____

How I Can Resolve It (Or Pray About It):

_____
_____
_____

Thoughts & Prayer:

_____
_____
_____
_____
_____
_____
_____
_____

Today's Entry

Date:_____   Exercise:_____   Water Intake: (1)(2)(3)(4)(5)(6)(7)(8)

5 Things I'm Thankful For:

1._____
2._____
3._____
4._____
5._____

My Quote Of The Day:

Today's Bible Reading (References & Notes):

_____
_____
_____

Prayer Requests/BIG Dreams:

_____
_____
_____

How I'm Feeling Today (Circle All That Apply):

* Happy * Stressed/Anxious * Peaceful * Tired
*Thankful * Sad * Angry *Lonely * Relieved
* Other:

Answers To Prayer:

_____
_____
_____

What's Bothering Me:

_____
_____

How I Can Resolve It (Or Pray About It):

_____
_____

Thoughts & Prayer:

_____
_____
_____
_____
_____
_____
_____
_____

Today's Entry

Date:_____   Exercise:_____   Water Intake: (1)(2)(3)(4)(5)(6)(7)(8)

5 Things I'm Thankful For:

1._____
2._____
3._____
4._____
5._____

My Quote Of The Day:

Today's Bible Reading (References & Notes):

_____
_____
_____

Prayer Requests/BIG Dreams:

_____
_____
_____

How I'm Feeling Today (Circle All That Apply):

* Happy * Stressed/Anxious * Peaceful * Tired
*Thankful * Sad * Angry *Lonely * Relieved
* Other:

Answers To Prayer:

_____
_____
_____

What's Bothering Me:

_____
_____

How I Can Resolve It (Or Pray About It):

_____
_____

Thoughts & Prayer:

_____
_____
_____
_____
_____
_____
_____
_____

Today's Entry

Date:_____ Exercise:_____ Water Intake: (1)(2)(3)(4)(5)(6)(7)(8)

5 Things I'm Thankful For:

1._____
2._____
3._____
4._____
5._____

My Quote Of The Day:

Today's Bible Reading (References & Notes):

_____
_____
_____
_____

Prayer Requests/BIG Dreams:

_____
_____
_____
_____

How I'm Feeling Today (Circle All That Apply):

* Happy * Stressed/Anxious * Peaceful * Tired
*Thankful * Sad * Angry *Lonely * Relieved
* Other:

Answers To Prayer:

_____
_____
_____

What's Bothering Me:

_____
_____

How I Can Resolve It (Or Pray About It):

_____
_____

Thoughts & Prayer:

_____
_____
_____
_____
_____
_____
_____
_____

Today's Entry

Date:_____ Exercise:_____ Water Intake: (1)(2)(3)(4)(5)(6)(7)(8)

5 Things I'm Thankful For:

1._____
2._____
3._____
4._____
5._____

My Quote Of The Day:

Today's Bible Reading (References & Notes):

_____
_____
_____

Prayer Requests/BIG Dreams:

_____
_____
_____

How I'm Feeling Today (Circle All That Apply):

* Happy * Stressed/Anxious * Peaceful * Tired
*Thankful * Sad * Angry *Lonely * Relieved
* Other:

Answers To Prayer:

_____
_____
_____

What's Bothering Me:

_____
_____

How I Can Resolve It (Or Pray About It):

_____
_____

Thoughts & Prayer:

_____
_____
_____
_____
_____
_____
_____
_____

Today's Entry

*Date:*_____   *Exercise:*_____   *Water Intake: (1)(2)(3)(4)(5)(6)(7)(8)*

5 Things I'm Thankful For:

1._____
2._____
3._____
4._____
5._____

My Quote Of The Day:

Today's Bible Reading (References & Notes):

_____
_____
_____

Prayer Requests/BIG Dreams:

_____
_____
_____

How I'm Feeling Today (Circle All That Apply):

* Happy * Stressed/Anxious * Peaceful * Tired
*Thankful * Sad * Angry *Lonely * Relieved
* Other:

Answers To Prayer:

_____
_____
_____

What's Bothering Me:

_____
_____

How I Can Resolve It (Or Pray About It):

_____
_____

Thoughts & Prayer:

_____
_____
_____
_____
_____
_____
_____

Today's Entry

Date:_____   Exercise:_____   Water Intake: (1)(2)(3)(4)(5)(6)(7)(8)

5 Things I'm Thankful For:

1._____
2._____
3._____
4._____
5._____

My Quote Of The Day:

Today's Bible Reading (References & Notes):

_____
_____
_____
_____

Prayer Requests/BIG Dreams:

_____
_____
_____
_____

How I'm Feeling Today (Circle All That Apply):

* Happy * Stressed/Anxious * Peaceful * Tired
*Thankful * Sad * Angry *Lonely * Relieved
* Other:

Answers To Prayer:

_____
_____
_____

What's Bothering Me:

_____
_____

How I Can Resolve It (Or Pray About It):

_____
_____
_____

Thoughts & Prayer:

_____
_____
_____
_____
_____
_____
_____
_____
_____

Today's Entry

Date:_____ Exercise:_____ Water Intake: (1)(2)(3)(4)(5)(6)(7)(8)

5 Things I'm Thankful For:

1._____
2._____
3._____
4._____
5._____

My Quote Of The Day:

Today's Bible Reading (References & Notes):

_____
_____
_____

Prayer Requests/BIG Dreams:

_____
_____
_____

How I'm Feeling Today (Circle All That Apply):

* Happy * Stressed/Anxious * Peaceful * Tired
*Thankful * Sad * Angry *Lonely * Relieved
* Other:

Answers To Prayer:

_____
_____
_____

What's Bothering Me:

_____
_____

How I Can Resolve It (Or Pray About It):

_____
_____

Thoughts & Prayer:

_____
_____
_____
_____
_____
_____
_____
_____

Today's Entry

Date:_____ Exercise:_____ Water Intake: (1)(2)(3)(4)(5)(6)(7)(8)

5 Things I'm Thankful For:

1._____
2._____
3._____
4._____
5._____

My Quote Of The Day:

Today's Bible Reading (References & Notes):

_____
_____
_____
_____

Prayer Requests/BIG Dreams:

_____
_____
_____

How I'm Feeling Today (Circle All That Apply):

* Happy * Stressed/Anxious * Peaceful * Tired
*Thankful * Sad * Angry *Lonely * Relieved
* Other:

Answers To Prayer:

_____
_____
_____

What's Bothering Me:

_____
_____

How I Can Resolve It (Or Pray About It):

_____
_____

Thoughts & Prayer:

_____
_____
_____
_____
_____
_____
_____
_____

Today's Entry

Date:_____ Exercise:_____ Water Intake: (1)(2)(3)(4)(5)(6)(7)(8)

5 Things I'm Thankful For:

1._____
2._____
3._____
4._____
5._____

My Quote Of The Day:

Today's Bible Reading (References & Notes):

_____
_____
_____

Prayer Requests/BIG Dreams:

_____
_____
_____

How I'm Feeling Today (Circle All That Apply):

* Happy * Stressed/Anxious * Peaceful * Tired
*Thankful * Sad * Angry *Lonely * Relieved
* Other:

Answers To Prayer:

_____
_____
_____

What's Bothering Me:

_____
_____

How I Can Resolve It (Or Pray About It):

_____
_____

Thoughts & Prayer:

_____
_____
_____
_____
_____
_____
_____
_____
_____

Today's Entry

Date:_____   Exercise:_____   Water Intake: (1)(2)(3)(4)(5)(6)(7)(8)

5 Things I'm Thankful For:

1._____
2._____
3._____
4._____
5._____

My Quote Of The Day:

Today's Bible Reading (References & Notes):

_____
_____
_____

Prayer Requests/BIG Dreams:

_____
_____
_____

How I'm Feeling Today (Circle All That Apply):

* Happy * Stressed/Anxious * Peaceful * Tired
*Thankful * Sad * Angry *Lonely * Relieved
* Other:

Answers To Prayer:

_____
_____
_____

What's Bothering Me:

_____
_____

How I Can Resolve It (Or Pray About It):

_____
_____

Thoughts & Prayer:

_____
_____
_____
_____
_____
_____
_____
_____

"Jesus looked at them
and said, 'With man
this is impossible, but
not with God; all things
are possible with God.'"
(Mark 10:27)

Today's Entry

Date:_____   Exercise:_____   Water Intake: (1)(2)(3)(4)(5)(6)(7)(8)

5 Things I'm Thankful For:

1._____
2._____
3._____
4._____
5._____

My Quote Of The Day:

Today's Bible Reading (References & Notes):

_____
_____
_____
_____

Prayer Requests/BIG Dreams:

_____
_____
_____

How I'm Feeling Today (Circle All That Apply):

* Happy * Stressed/Anxious * Peaceful * Tired
*Thankful * Sad * Angry *Lonely * Relieved
* Other:

Answers To Prayer:

_____
_____
_____

What's Bothering Me:

_____
_____

How I Can Resolve It (Or Pray About It):

_____
_____

Thoughts & Prayer:

_____
_____
_____
_____
_____
_____
_____
_____

Today's Entry

Date: _____ *Exercise:* _____ *Water Intake: (1)(2)(3)(4)(5)(6)(7)(8)*

5 Things I'm Thankful For:

1. _____
2. _____
3. _____
4. _____
5. _____

My Quote Of The Day:

Today's Bible Reading (References & Notes):

_____
_____
_____

Prayer Requests/BIG Dreams:

_____
_____
_____

How I'm Feeling Today (Circle All That Apply):

* Happy * Stressed/Anxious * Peaceful * Tired
*Thankful * Sad * Angry *Lonely * Relieved
* Other:

Answers To Prayer:

_____
_____
_____

What's Bothering Me:

_____
_____

How I Can Resolve It (Or Pray About It):

_____
_____

Thoughts & Prayer:

_____
_____
_____
_____
_____
_____
_____
_____

Today's Entry

Date:_____   Exercise:_____   Water Intake: (1)(2)(3)(4)(5)(6)(7)(8)

5 Things I'm Thankful For:

1._____
2._____
3._____
4._____
5._____

My Quote Of The Day:

Today's Bible Reading (References & Notes):

_____
_____
_____
_____

Prayer Requests/BIG Dreams:

_____
_____
_____
_____

How I'm Feeling Today (Circle All That Apply):

* Happy * Stressed/Anxious * Peaceful * Tired
*Thankful * Sad * Angry *Lonely * Relieved
* Other:

Answers To Prayer:

_____
_____
_____

What's Bothering Me:

_____
_____

How I Can Resolve It (Or Pray About It):

_____
_____
_____

Thoughts & Prayer:

_____
_____
_____
_____
_____
_____
_____
_____
_____

Today's Entry

Date:_____   Exercise:_____   Water Intake: (1)(2)(3)(4)(5)(6)(7)(8)

5 Things I'm Thankful For:

1._____
2._____
3._____
4._____
5._____

My Quote Of The Day:

Today's Bible Reading (References & Notes):

_____
_____
_____

Prayer Requests/BIG Dreams:

_____
_____
_____

How I'm Feeling Today (Circle All That Apply):

* Happy * Stressed/Anxious * Peaceful * Tired
*Thankful * Sad * Angry *Lonely * Relieved
* Other:

Answers To Prayer:

_____
_____
_____

What's Bothering Me:

_____
_____

How I Can Resolve It (Or Pray About It):

_____
_____

Thoughts & Prayer:

_____
_____
_____
_____
_____
_____
_____
_____

Today's Entry

Date:_____ Exercise:_____ Water Intake: (1)(2)(3)(4)(5)(6)(7)(8)

5 Things I'm Thankful For:

1._____
2._____
3._____
4._____
5._____

My Quote Of The Day:

Today's Bible Reading (References & Notes):

_____
_____
_____
_____

Prayer Requests/BIG Dreams:

_____
_____
_____

How I'm Feeling Today (Circle All That Apply):

* Happy * Stressed/Anxious * Peaceful * Tired
*Thankful * Sad * Angry *Lonely * Relieved
* Other:

Answers To Prayer:

_____
_____
_____

What's Bothering Me:

_____
_____

How I Can Resolve It (Or Pray About It):

_____
_____

Thoughts & Prayer:

_____
_____
_____
_____
_____
_____
_____
_____

Today's Entry

Date:_____ Exercise:_____ Water Intake: (1)(2)(3)(4)(5)(6)(7)(8)

5 Things I'm Thankful For:

1._____
2._____
3._____
4._____
5._____

My Quote Of The Day:

Today's Bible Reading (References & Notes):

_____
_____
_____

Prayer Requests/BIG Dreams:

_____
_____
_____

How I'm Feeling Today (Circle All That Apply):

* Happy * Stressed/Anxious * Peaceful * Tired
*Thankful * Sad * Angry *Lonely * Relieved
* Other:

Answers To Prayer:

_____
_____
_____

What's Bothering Me:

_____
_____

How I Can Resolve It (Or Pray About It):

_____
_____

Thoughts & Prayer:

_____
_____
_____
_____
_____
_____
_____
_____
_____

Today's Entry

Date:_____   Exercise:_____   Water Intake: (1)(2)(3)(4)(5)(6)(7)(8)

5 Things I'm Thankful For:

1._____
2._____
3._____
4._____
5._____

My Quote Of The Day:

Today's Bible Reading (References & Notes):

_____
_____
_____

Prayer Requests/BIG Dreams:

_____
_____
_____

How I'm Feeling Today (Circle All That Apply):

* Happy * Stressed/Anxious * Peaceful * Tired
*Thankful * Sad * Angry *Lonely * Relieved
* Other:

Answers To Prayer:

_____
_____
_____

What's Bothering Me:

_____
_____

How I Can Resolve It (Or Pray About It):

_____
_____

Thoughts & Prayer:

_____
_____
_____
_____
_____
_____
_____
_____

Today's Entry

Date:_____ Exercise:_____ Water Intake: (1)(2)(3)(4)(5)(6)(7)(8)

5 Things I'm Thankful For:

1._____
2._____
3._____
4._____
5._____

My Quote Of The Day:

Today's Bible Reading (References & Notes):

_____
_____
_____

Prayer Requests/BIG Dreams:

_____
_____
_____

How I'm Feeling Today (Circle All That Apply):

* Happy * Stressed/Anxious * Peaceful * Tired
*Thankful * Sad * Angry *Lonely * Relieved
* Other:

Answers To Prayer:

_____
_____
_____

What's Bothering Me:

_____
_____

How I Can Resolve It (Or Pray About It):

_____
_____

Thoughts & Prayer:

_____
_____
_____
_____
_____
_____
_____
_____

Today's Entry

Date:_____   Exercise:_____   Water Intake: (1)(2)(3)(4)(5)(6)(7)(8)

5 Things I'm Thankful For:

1._____
2._____
3._____
4._____
5._____

My Quote Of The Day:

Today's Bible Reading (References & Notes):

_____
_____
_____

Prayer Requests/BIG Dreams:

_____
_____
_____

How I'm Feeling Today (Circle All That Apply):

* Happy * Stressed/Anxious * Peaceful * Tired
*Thankful * Sad * Angry *Lonely *Relieved
* Other:

Answers To Prayer:

_____
_____
_____

What's Bothering Me:

_____
_____

How I Can Resolve It (Or Pray About It):

_____
_____

Thoughts & Prayer:

_____
_____
_____
_____
_____
_____
_____

Today's Entry

Date:_____ Exercise:_____ Water Intake: (1)(2)(3)(4)(5)(6)(7)(8)

5 Things I'm Thankful For:

1._____
2._____
3._____
4._____
5._____

My Quote Of The Day:

Today's Bible Reading (References & Notes):

_____
_____
_____

Prayer Requests/BIG Dreams:

_____
_____
_____

How I'm Feeling Today (Circle All That Apply):

* Happy * Stressed/Anxious * Peaceful * Tired
*Thankful * Sad * Angry *Lonely * Relieved
* Other:

Answers To Prayer:

_____
_____
_____

What's Bothering Me:

_____
_____

How I Can Resolve It (Or Pray About It):

_____
_____

Thoughts & Prayer:

_____
_____
_____
_____
_____
_____
_____
_____

Today's Entry

Date:_____ Exercise:_____ Water Intake: (1)(2)(3)(4)(5)(6)(7)(8)

5 Things I'm Thankful For:

1._____
2._____
3._____
4._____
5._____

My Quote Of The Day:

Today's Bible Reading (References & Notes):

_____
_____
_____
_____

Prayer Requests/BIG Dreams:

_____
_____
_____
_____

How I'm Feeling Today (Circle All That Apply):

* Happy * Stressed/Anxious * Peaceful * Tired
*Thankful * Sad * Angry *Lonely * Relieved
* Other:

Answers To Prayer:

_____
_____
_____

What's Bothering Me:

_____
_____

How I Can Resolve It (Or Pray About It):

_____
_____
_____

Thoughts & Prayer:

_____
_____
_____
_____
_____
_____
_____
_____
_____

Today's Entry

Date:_____ Exercise:_____ Water Intake: (1)(2)(3)(4)(5)(6)(7)(8)

5 Things I'm Thankful For:

1._____
2._____
3._____
4._____
5._____

My Quote Of The Day:

Today's Bible Reading (References & Notes):

_____
_____
_____

Prayer Requests/BIG Dreams:

_____
_____
_____

How I'm Feeling Today (Circle All That Apply):

* Happy * Stressed/Anxious * Peaceful * Tired
*Thankful * Sad * Angry *Lonely * Relieved
* Other:

Answers To Prayer:

_____
_____
_____

What's Bothering Me:

_____
_____

How I Can Resolve It (Or Pray About It):

_____
_____

Thoughts & Prayer:

_____
_____
_____
_____
_____
_____
_____

Today's Entry

Date:_____   Exercise:_____   Water Intake: (1)(2)(3)(4)(5)(6)(7)(8)

5 Things I'm Thankful For:

1._____
2._____
3._____
4._____
5._____

My Quote Of The Day:

Today's Bible Reading (References & Notes):

_____
_____
_____

Prayer Requests/BIG Dreams:

_____
_____
_____
_____

How I'm Feeling Today (Circle All That Apply):

* Happy * Stressed/Anxious * Peaceful * Tired
*Thankful * Sad * Angry *Lonely * Relieved
* Other:

Answers To Prayer:

_____
_____
_____

What's Bothering Me:

_____
_____

How I Can Resolve It (Or Pray About It):

_____
_____

Thoughts & Prayer:

_____
_____
_____
_____
_____
_____
_____
_____

Today's Entry

Date:_____   Exercise:_____   Water Intake: (1)(2)(3)(4)(5)(6)(7)(8)

5 Things I'm Thankful For:

1._____
2._____
3._____
4._____
5._____

My Quote Of The Day:

Today's Bible Reading (References & Notes):

_____
_____
_____

Prayer Requests/BIG Dreams:

_____
_____
_____

How I'm Feeling Today (Circle All That Apply):

* Happy * Stressed/Anxious * Peaceful * Tired
*Thankful * Sad * Angry *Lonely * Relieved
* Other:

Answers To Prayer:

_____
_____
_____

What's Bothering Me:

_____
_____

How I Can Resolve It (Or Pray About It):

_____
_____

Thoughts & Prayer:

_____
_____
_____
_____
_____
_____
_____
_____
_____

Today's Entry

Date:_____ Exercise:_____ Water Intake: (1)(2)(3)(4)(5)(6)(7)(8)

5 Things I'm Thankful For:

1._____
2._____
3._____
4._____
5._____

My Quote Of The Day:

Today's Bible Reading (References & Notes):

_____
_____
_____

Prayer Requests/BIG Dreams:

_____
_____
_____

How I'm Feeling Today (Circle All That Apply):

* Happy * Stressed/Anxious * Peaceful * Tired
*Thankful * Sad * Angry *Lonely * Relieved
* Other:

Answers To Prayer:

_____
_____
_____

What's Bothering Me:

_____
_____

How I Can Resolve It (Or Pray About It):

_____
_____

Thoughts & Prayer:

_____
_____
_____
_____
_____
_____
_____
_____

Today's Entry

Date:_____   Exercise:_____   Water Intake: (1)(2)(3)(4)(5)(6)(7)(8)

5 Things I'm Thankful For:

1._____
2._____
3._____
4._____
5._____

My Quote Of The Day:

Today's Bible Reading (References & Notes):
_____
_____
_____

Prayer Requests/BIG Dreams:
_____
_____
_____

How I'm Feeling Today (Circle All That Apply):

* Happy * Stressed/Anxious * Peaceful * Tired
*Thankful * Sad * Angry *Lonely * Relieved
* Other:

Answers To Prayer:
_____
_____
_____

What's Bothering Me:
_____
_____

How I Can Resolve It (Or Pray About It):
_____
_____

Thoughts & Prayer:
_____
_____
_____
_____
_____
_____
_____
_____

Today's Entry

Date:_____   Exercise:_____   Water Intake: (1)(2)(3)(4)(5)(6)(7)(8)

5 Things I'm Thankful For:

1._____
2._____
3._____
4._____
5._____

My Quote Of The Day:

Today's Bible Reading (References & Notes):

_____
_____
_____

Prayer Requests/BIG Dreams:

_____
_____
_____

How I'm Feeling Today (Circle All That Apply):

* Happy * Stressed/Anxious * Peaceful * Tired
*Thankful * Sad * Angry *Lonely * Relieved
* Other:

Answers To Prayer:

_____
_____
_____

What's Bothering Me:

_____
_____

How I Can Resolve It (Or Pray About It):

_____
_____

Thoughts & Prayer:

_____
_____
_____
_____
_____
_____
_____
_____

Today's Entry

*Date:*_____ *Exercise:*_____ *Water Intake: (1)(2)(3)(4)(5)(6)(7)(8)*

5 Things I'm Thankful For:

1._____
2._____
3._____
4._____
5._____

My Quote Of The Day:

Today's Bible Reading (References & Notes):

_____
_____
_____

Prayer Requests/BIG Dreams:

_____
_____
_____

How I'm Feeling Today (Circle All That Apply):

* Happy * Stressed/Anxious * Peaceful * Tired
*Thankful * Sad * Angry *Lonely * Relieved
* Other:

Answers To Prayer:

_____
_____
_____

What's Bothering Me:

_____
_____

How I Can Resolve It (Or Pray About It):

_____
_____

Thoughts & Prayer:

_____
_____
_____
_____
_____
_____
_____
_____

Today's Entry

Date:_____ Exercise:_____ Water Intake: (1)(2)(3)(4)(5)(6)(7)(8)

5 Things I'm Thankful For:

1._____
2._____
3._____
4._____
5._____

My Quote Of The Day:

Today's Bible Reading (References & Notes):

_____
_____
_____
_____

Prayer Requests/BIG Dreams:

_____
_____
_____
_____

How I'm Feeling Today (Circle All That Apply):

* Happy * Stressed/Anxious * Peaceful * Tired
*Thankful * Sad * Angry *Lonely * Relieved
* Other:

Answers To Prayer:

_____
_____
_____

What's Bothering Me:

_____
_____

How I Can Resolve It (Or Pray About It):

_____
_____
_____

Thoughts & Prayer:

_____
_____
_____
_____
_____
_____
_____
_____
_____

Today's Entry

Date:_____   Exercise:_____   Water Intake: (1)(2)(3)(4)(5)(6)(7)(8)

5 Things I'm Thankful For:

1._____
2._____
3._____
4._____
5._____

My Quote Of The Day:

Today's Bible Reading (References & Notes):

_____
_____
_____

Prayer Requests/BIG Dreams:

_____
_____
_____

How I'm Feeling Today (Circle All That Apply):

* Happy * Stressed/Anxious * Peaceful * Tired
*Thankful * Sad * Angry *Lonely * Relieved
* Other:

Answers To Prayer:

_____
_____
_____

What's Bothering Me:

_____
_____

How I Can Resolve It (Or Pray About It):

_____
_____

Thoughts & Prayer:

_____
_____
_____
_____
_____
_____
_____
_____
_____

Today's Entry

Date:_____ Exercise:_____ Water Intake: (1)(2)(3)(4)(5)(6)(7)(8)

5 Things I'm Thankful For:

1._____
2._____
3._____
4._____
5._____

My Quote Of The Day:

Today's Bible Reading (References & Notes):

_____
_____
_____

Prayer Requests/BIG Dreams:

_____
_____
_____
_____

How I'm Feeling Today (Circle All That Apply):

* Happy * Stressed/Anxious * Peaceful * Tired
*Thankful * Sad * Angry *Lonely * Relieved
* Other:

Answers To Prayer:

_____
_____
_____

What's Bothering Me:

_____
_____

How I Can Resolve It (Or Pray About It):

_____
_____

Thoughts & Prayer:

_____
_____
_____
_____
_____
_____
_____

Today's Entry

*Date:*_____ *Exercise:*_____ *Water Intake: (1)(2)(3)(4)(5)(6)(7)(8)*

5 Things I'm Thankful For:

1._____
2._____
3._____
4._____
5._____

My Quote Of The Day:

Today's Bible Reading (References & Notes):

_____
_____
_____

Prayer Requests/BIG Dreams:

_____
_____
_____

How I'm Feeling Today (Circle All That Apply):

* Happy * Stressed/Anxious * Peaceful * Tired
*Thankful * Sad * Angry *Lonely * Relieved
* Other:

Answers To Prayer:

_____
_____
_____

What's Bothering Me:

_____
_____

How I Can Resolve It (Or Pray About It):

_____
_____

Thoughts & Prayer:

_____
_____
_____
_____
_____
_____
_____
_____

Today's Entry

Date:_____ Exercise:_____ Water Intake: (1)(2)(3)(4)(5)(6)(7)(8)

5 Things I'm Thankful For:

1._____
2._____
3._____
4._____
5._____

My Quote Of The Day:

Today's Bible Reading (References & Notes):

_____
_____
_____

Prayer Requests/BIG Dreams:

_____
_____
_____

How I'm Feeling Today (Circle All That Apply):

* Happy * Stressed/Anxious * Peaceful * Tired
*Thankful * Sad * Angry *Lonely * Relieved
* Other:

Answers To Prayer:

_____
_____
_____

What's Bothering Me:

_____
_____

How I Can Resolve It (Or Pray About It):

_____
_____

Thoughts & Prayer:

_____
_____
_____
_____
_____
_____
_____
_____

Today's Entry

Date:_____   Exercise:_____   Water Intake: (1)(2)(3)(4)(5)(6)(7)(8)

5 Things I'm Thankful For:

1._____
2._____
3._____
4._____
5._____

My Quote Of The Day:

Today's Bible Reading (References & Notes):

_____
_____
_____

Prayer Requests/BIG Dreams:

_____
_____
_____

How I'm Feeling Today (Circle All That Apply):

* Happy * Stressed/Anxious * Peaceful * Tired
*Thankful * Sad * Angry *Lonely * Relieved
* Other:

Answers To Prayer:

_____
_____
_____

What's Bothering Me:

_____
_____

How I Can Resolve It (Or Pray About It):

_____
_____

Thoughts & Prayer:

_____
_____
_____
_____
_____
_____
_____
_____

Today's Entry

Date:_____   Exercise:_____   Water Intake: (1)(2)(3)(4)(5)(6)(7)(8)

5 Things I'm Thankful For:

1._____
2._____
3._____
4._____
5._____

My Quote Of The Day:

Today's Bible Reading (References & Notes):

_____
_____
_____
_____

Prayer Requests/BIG Dreams:

_____
_____
_____

How I'm Feeling Today (Circle All That Apply):

* Happy * Stressed/Anxious * Peaceful * Tired
*Thankful * Sad * Angry *Lonely * Relieved
* Other:

Answers To Prayer:

_____
_____
_____

What's Bothering Me:

_____
_____

How I Can Resolve It (Or Pray About It):

_____
_____

Thoughts & Prayer:

_____
_____
_____
_____
_____
_____
_____
_____

Today's Entry

*Date:*_____ *Exercise:*_____ *Water Intake: (1)(2)(3)(4)(5)(6)(7)(8)*

5 Things I'm Thankful For:

1._____
2._____
3._____
4._____
5._____

My Quote Of The Day:

Today's Bible Reading (References & Notes):

_____
_____
_____

Prayer Requests/BIG Dreams:

_____
_____
_____

How I'm Feeling Today (Circle All That Apply):

* Happy * Stressed/Anxious * Peaceful * Tired
*Thankful * Sad * Angry *Lonely * Relieved
* Other:

Answers To Prayer:

_____
_____
_____

What's Bothering Me:

_____
_____

How I Can Resolve It (Or Pray About It):

_____
_____

Thoughts & Prayer:

_____
_____
_____
_____
_____
_____
_____
_____

Today's Entry

Date: _____ Exercise: _____ Water Intake: (1)(2)(3)(4)(5)(6)(7)(8)

5 Things I'm Thankful For:

1. _____
2. _____
3. _____
4. _____
5. _____

My Quote Of The Day:

Today's Bible Reading (References & Notes):

_____
_____
_____
_____

Prayer Requests/BIG Dreams:

_____
_____
_____
_____

How I'm Feeling Today (Circle All That Apply):

* Happy * Stressed/Anxious * Peaceful * Tired
*Thankful * Sad * Angry *Lonely * Relieved
* Other:

Answers To Prayer:

_____
_____
_____

What's Bothering Me:

_____
_____

How I Can Resolve It (Or Pray About It):

_____
_____

Thoughts & Prayer:

_____
_____
_____
_____
_____
_____
_____
_____

Today's Entry

Date:_____ Exercise:_____ Water Intake: (1)(2)(3)(4)(5)(6)(7)(8)

5 Things I'm Thankful For:

1._____
2._____
3._____
4._____
5._____

My Quote Of The Day:

Today's Bible Reading (References & Notes):

_____
_____
_____

Prayer Requests/BIG Dreams:

_____
_____
_____

How I'm Feeling Today (Circle All That Apply):

* Happy * Stressed/Anxious * Peaceful * Tired
*Thankful * Sad * Angry *Lonely * Relieved
* Other:

Answers To Prayer:

_____
_____
_____

What's Bothering Me:

_____
_____

How I Can Resolve It (Or Pray About It):

_____
_____

Thoughts & Prayer:

_____
_____
_____
_____
_____
_____
_____
_____

Today's Entry

Date:_____   Exercise:_____   Water Intake: (1)(2)(3)(4)(5)(6)(7)(8)

5 Things I'm Thankful For:

1._____
2._____
3._____
4._____
5._____

My Quote Of The Day:

Today's Bible Reading (References & Notes):

_____
_____
_____

Prayer Requests/BIG Dreams:

_____
_____
_____

How I'm Feeling Today (Circle All That Apply):

* Happy * Stressed/Anxious * Peaceful * Tired
*Thankful * Sad * Angry *Lonely * Relieved
 * Other:

Answers To Prayer:

_____
_____
_____

What's Bothering Me:

_____
_____

How I Can Resolve It (Or Pray About It):

_____
_____

Thoughts & Prayer:

_____
_____
_____
_____
_____
_____
_____
_____

Today's Entry

Date:_____   Exercise:_____   Water Intake: (1)(2)(3)(4)(5)(6)(7)(8)

5 Things I'm Thankful For:

1._____
2._____
3._____
4._____
5._____

My Quote Of The Day:

Today's Bible Reading (References & Notes):

_____
_____
_____

Prayer Requests/BIG Dreams:

_____
_____
_____

How I'm Feeling Today (Circle All That Apply):

* Happy * Stressed/Anxious * Peaceful * Tired
*Thankful * Sad * Angry *Lonely * Relieved
* Other:

Answers To Prayer:

_____
_____
_____

What's Bothering Me:

_____
_____

How I Can Resolve It (Or Pray About It):

_____
_____

Thoughts & Prayer:

_____
_____
_____
_____
_____
_____
_____
_____

Today's Entry

Date:_____ Exercise:_____ Water Intake: (1)(2)(3)(4)(5)(6)(7)(8)

5 Things I'm Thankful For:

1._____
2._____
3._____
4._____
5._____

My Quote Of The Day:

Today's Bible Reading (References & Notes):

_____
_____
_____

Prayer Requests/BIG Dreams:

_____
_____
_____

How I'm Feeling Today (Circle All That Apply):

* Happy * Stressed/Anxious * Peaceful * Tired
*Thankful * Sad * Angry *Lonely * Relieved
* Other:

Answers To Prayer:

_____
_____
_____

What's Bothering Me:

_____
_____

How I Can Resolve It (Or Pray About It):

_____
_____

Thoughts & Prayer:

_____
_____
_____
_____
_____
_____
_____
_____

Today's Entry

Date:_____   Exercise:_____   Water Intake: (1)(2)(3)(4)(5)(6)(7)(8)

5 Things I'm Thankful For:

1._____
2._____
3._____
4._____
5._____

My Quote Of The Day:

Today's Bible Reading (References & Notes):

_____
_____
_____

Prayer Requests/BIG Dreams:

_____
_____
_____

How I'm Feeling Today (Circle All That Apply):

* Happy * Stressed/Anxious * Peaceful * Tired
*Thankful * Sad * Angry *Lonely * Relieved
* Other:

Answers To Prayer:

_____
_____
_____

What's Bothering Me:

_____
_____

How I Can Resolve It (Or Pray About It):

_____
_____

Thoughts & Prayer:

_____
_____
_____
_____
_____
_____
_____
_____

Today's Entry

Date:_____   Exercise:_____   Water Intake: (1)(2)(3)(4)(5)(6)(7)(8)

5 Things I'm Thankful For:

1._____
2._____
3._____
4._____
5._____

My Quote Of The Day:

Today's Bible Reading (References & Notes):

_____
_____
_____

Prayer Requests/BIG Dreams:

_____
_____
_____
_____

How I'm Feeling Today (Circle All That Apply):

* Happy * Stressed/Anxious * Peaceful * Tired
*Thankful * Sad * Angry *Lonely * Relieved
* Other:

Answers To Prayer:

_____
_____
_____

What's Bothering Me:

_____
_____

How I Can Resolve It (Or Pray About It):

_____
_____

Thoughts & Prayer:

_____
_____
_____
_____
_____
_____
_____
_____

Today's Entry

*Date:*_____ *Exercise:*_____ *Water Intake:* (1)(2)(3)(4)(5)(6)(7)(8)

5 Things I'm Thankful For:

1._____
2._____
3._____
4._____
5._____

My Quote Of The Day:

Today's Bible Reading (References & Notes):

_____
_____
_____

Prayer Requests/BIG Dreams:

_____
_____
_____

How I'm Feeling Today (Circle All That Apply):

* Happy * Stressed/Anxious * Peaceful * Tired
*Thankful * Sad * Angry *Lonely * Relieved
* Other:

Answers To Prayer:

_____
_____
_____

What's Bothering Me:

_____
_____

How I Can Resolve It (Or Pray About It):

_____
_____

Thoughts & Prayer:

_____
_____
_____
_____
_____
_____
_____
_____

Today's Entry

Date:_____ Exercise:_____ Water Intake: (1)(2)(3)(4)(5)(6)(7)(8)

5 Things I'm Thankful For:

1._____
2._____
3._____
4._____
5._____

My Quote Of The Day:

Today's Bible Reading (References & Notes):

_____
_____
_____

Prayer Requests/BIG Dreams:

_____
_____
_____

How I'm Feeling Today (Circle All That Apply):

* Happy * Stressed/Anxious * Peaceful * Tired
*Thankful * Sad * Angry *Lonely * Relieved
* Other:

Answers To Prayer:

_____
_____
_____

What's Bothering Me:

_____
_____

How I Can Resolve It (Or Pray About It):

_____
_____

Thoughts & Prayer:

_____
_____
_____
_____
_____
_____
_____
_____

Today's Entry

Date:_____ Exercise:_____ Water Intake: (1)(2)(3)(4)(5)(6)(7)(8)

5 Things I'm Thankful For:

1._____
2._____
3._____
4._____
5._____

My Quote Of The Day:

Today's Bible Reading (References & Notes):

_____
_____
_____

Prayer Requests/BIG Dreams:

_____
_____
_____

How I'm Feeling Today (Circle All That Apply):

* Happy * Stressed/Anxious * Peaceful * Tired
*Thankful * Sad * Angry *Lonely * Relieved
* Other:

Answers To Prayer:

_____
_____
_____

What's Bothering Me:

_____
_____

How I Can Resolve It (Or Pray About It):

_____
_____

Thoughts & Prayer:

_____
_____
_____
_____
_____
_____
_____
_____

Today's Entry

Date:_____ Exercise:_____ Water Intake: (1)(2)(3)(4)(5)(6)(7)(8)

5 Things I'm Thankful For:

1._____
2._____
3._____
4._____
5._____

My Quote Of The Day:

Today's Bible Reading (References & Notes):

_____
_____
_____

Prayer Requests/BIG Dreams:

_____
_____
_____

How I'm Feeling Today (Circle All That Apply):

* Happy * Stressed/Anxious * Peaceful * Tired
*Thankful * Sad * Angry *Lonely * Relieved
* Other:

Answers To Prayer:

_____
_____
_____

What's Bothering Me:

_____
_____

How I Can Resolve It (Or Pray About It):

_____
_____

Thoughts & Prayer:

_____
_____
_____
_____
_____
_____
_____
_____
_____

Today's Entry

Date:_____ Exercise:_____ Water Intake: (1)(2)(3)(4)(5)(6)(7)(8)

5 Things I'm Thankful For:

1._____
2._____
3._____
4._____
5._____

My Quote Of The Day:

Today's Bible Reading (References & Notes):

_____
_____
_____

Prayer Requests/BIG Dreams:

_____
_____
_____

How I'm Feeling Today (Circle All That Apply):

* Happy * Stressed/Anxious * Peaceful * Tired
*Thankful * Sad * Angry *Lonely * Relieved
* Other:

Answers To Prayer:

_____
_____
_____

What's Bothering Me:

_____
_____

How I Can Resolve It (Or Pray About It):

_____
_____

Thoughts & Prayer:

_____
_____
_____
_____
_____
_____
_____
_____

Today's Entry

Date:_____ Exercise:_____ Water Intake: (1)(2)(3)(4)(5)(6)(7)(8)

5 Things I'm Thankful For:

1._____
2._____
3._____
4._____
5._____

My Quote Of The Day:

Today's Bible Reading (References & Notes):

_____
_____
_____

Prayer Requests/BIG Dreams:

_____
_____
_____

How I'm Feeling Today (Circle All That Apply):

* Happy * Stressed/Anxious * Peaceful * Tired
*Thankful * Sad * Angry *Lonely * Relieved
* Other:

Answers To Prayer:

_____
_____
_____

What's Bothering Me:

_____
_____

How I Can Resolve It (Or Pray About It):

_____
_____

Thoughts & Prayer:

_____
_____
_____
_____
_____
_____
_____
_____

Today's Entry

Date:_____   Exercise:_____   Water Intake: (1)(2)(3)(4)(5)(6)(7)(8)

5 Things I'm Thankful For:

1._____
2._____
3._____
4._____
5._____

My Quote Of The Day:

Today's Bible Reading (References & Notes):

_____
_____
_____

Prayer Requests/BIG Dreams:

_____
_____
_____

How I'm Feeling Today (Circle All That Apply):

* Happy * Stressed/Anxious * Peaceful * Tired
*Thankful * Sad * Angry *Lonely * Relieved
* Other:

Answers To Prayer:

_____
_____
_____

What's Bothering Me:

_____
_____

How I Can Resolve It (Or Pray About It):

_____
_____

Thoughts & Prayer:

_____
_____
_____
_____
_____
_____
_____
_____

Today's Entry

Date:_____ Exercise:_____ Water Intake: (1)(2)(3)(4)(5)(6)(7)(8)

5 Things I'm Thankful For:

1._____
2._____
3._____
4._____
5._____

My Quote Of The Day:

Today's Bible Reading (References & Notes):

_____
_____
_____

Prayer Requests/BIG Dreams:

_____
_____
_____

How I'm Feeling Today (Circle All That Apply):

* Happy * Stressed/Anxious * Peaceful * Tired
*Thankful * Sad * Angry *Lonely * Relieved
* Other:

Answers To Prayer:

_____
_____
_____

What's Bothering Me:

_____
_____

How I Can Resolve It (Or Pray About It):

_____
_____

Thoughts & Prayer:

_____
_____
_____
_____
_____
_____
_____

Today's Entry

Date:_____   Exercise:_____   Water Intake: (1)(2)(3)(4)(5)(6)(7)(8)

5 Things I'm Thankful For:

1._____
2._____
3._____
4._____
5._____

My Quote Of The Day:

Today's Bible Reading (References & Notes):

_____
_____
_____

Prayer Requests/BIG Dreams:

_____
_____
_____

How I'm Feeling Today (Circle All That Apply):

* Happy * Stressed/Anxious * Peaceful * Tired
*Thankful * Sad * Angry *Lonely * Relieved
* Other:

Answers To Prayer:

_____
_____
_____

What's Bothering Me:

_____
_____

How I Can Resolve It (Or Pray About It):

_____
_____

Thoughts & Prayer:

_____
_____
_____
_____
_____
_____
_____
_____

Today's Entry

Date:_____   Exercise:_____   Water Intake: (1)(2)(3)(4)(5)(6)(7)(8)

5 Things I'm Thankful For:

1._____
2._____
3._____
4._____
5._____

My Quote Of The Day:

Today's Bible Reading (References & Notes):

_____
_____
_____

Prayer Requests/BIG Dreams:

_____
_____
_____

How I'm Feeling Today (Circle All That Apply):

* Happy * Stressed/Anxious * Peaceful * Tired
*Thankful * Sad * Angry *Lonely * Relieved
* Other:

Answers To Prayer:

_____
_____
_____

What's Bothering Me:

_____
_____

How I Can Resolve It (Or Pray About It):

_____
_____

Thoughts & Prayer:

_____
_____
_____
_____
_____
_____
_____
_____

Today's Entry

Date:_____ Exercise:_____ Water Intake: (1)(2)(3)(4)(5)(6)(7)(8)

5 Things I'm Thankful For:

1._____
2._____
3._____
4._____
5._____

My Quote Of The Day:

Today's Bible Reading (References & Notes):

_____
_____
_____

Prayer Requests/BIG Dreams:

_____
_____
_____

How I'm Feeling Today (Circle All That Apply):

* Happy * Stressed/Anxious * Peaceful * Tired
*Thankful * Sad * Angry *Lonely * Relieved
* Other:

Answers To Prayer:

_____
_____
_____

What's Bothering Me:

_____
_____

How I Can Resolve It (Or Pray About It):

_____
_____

Thoughts & Prayer:

_____
_____
_____
_____
_____
_____
_____
_____
_____

Today's Entry

Date:_____ Exercise:_____ Water Intake: (1)(2)(3)(4)(5)(6)(7)(8)

5 Things I'm Thankful For:

1._____
2._____
3._____
4._____
5._____

My Quote Of The Day:

Today's Bible Reading (References & Notes):

_____
_____
_____

Prayer Requests/BIG Dreams:

_____
_____
_____

How I'm Feeling Today (Circle All That Apply):

* Happy * Stressed/Anxious * Peaceful * Tired
*Thankful * Sad * Angry *Lonely * Relieved
* Other:

Answers To Prayer:

_____
_____
_____

What's Bothering Me:

_____
_____

How I Can Resolve It (Or Pray About It):

_____
_____

Thoughts & Prayer:

_____
_____
_____
_____
_____
_____
_____

Today's Entry

*Date:*_____ *Exercise:*_____ *Water Intake: (1)(2)(3)(4)(5)(6)(7)(8)*

5 Things I'm Thankful For:

1._____
2._____
3._____
4._____
5._____

My Quote Of The Day:

Today's Bible Reading (References & Notes):

_____
_____
_____
_____

Prayer Requests/BIG Dreams:

_____
_____
_____
_____

How I'm Feeling Today (Circle All That Apply):

* Happy * Stressed/Anxious * Peaceful * Tired
*Thankful * Sad * Angry *Lonely * Relieved
* Other:

Answers To Prayer:

_____
_____
_____

What's Bothering Me:

_____
_____

How I Can Resolve It (Or Pray About It):

_____
_____

Thoughts & Prayer:

_____
_____
_____
_____
_____
_____
_____
_____

Today's Entry

Date:_____ Exercise:_____ Water Intake: (1)(2)(3)(4)(5)(6)(7)(8)

5 Things I'm Thankful For:

1._____
2._____
3._____
4._____
5._____

My Quote Of The Day:

Today's Bible Reading (References & Notes):

_____
_____
_____

Prayer Requests/BIG Dreams:

_____
_____
_____

How I'm Feeling Today (Circle All That Apply):

* Happy * Stressed/Anxious * Peaceful * Tired
*Thankful * Sad * Angry *Lonely * Relieved
* Other:

Answers To Prayer:

_____
_____
_____

What's Bothering Me:

_____
_____

How I Can Resolve It (Or Pray About It):

_____
_____

Thoughts & Prayer:

_____
_____
_____
_____
_____
_____
_____
_____

"May the God of hope
fill you with all joy
and peace as you trust
in Him..."
(Rom. 15:13)

Made in the USA
Coppell, TX
10 June 2020

27333569R00083